The Forsaken Merman
and other story poems

Edited by Vic Parker

Published by Hodder Children's Books 1998

10 9 8 7 6 5 4 3 2 1

ISBN 0340 68997 8

Printed and bound in Great Britain

Hodder Children's Books
A division of Hodder Headline plc
338 Euston Road
London NW1 3BH

The FOrsaken Merman and other story poems

selected by Berlie Doherty

illustrations by Nick Maland

Hodder Children's Books

a division of Hodder Headline plc

To the Arvon Foundation,
where poets are at home

Contents

The Forsaken Merman

Come, dear children, let us away;
Down and away below!
Now my brothers call from the bay,
Now the great winds shoreward blow,
Now the salt tides seaward flow;
Now the wild white horses play,
Champ and chafe and toss in the spray.
Children dear, let us away!
This way, this way!

Call her once before you go –
Call once yet!
In a voice that she will know:
'Margaret! Margaret!'
Children's voices should be dear
(Call once more) to a mother's ear;
Children's voices, wild with pain –
Surely she will come again!
Call her once and come away;
This way, this way!
'Mother dear, we cannot stay!
The wild white horses foam and fret.'
Margaret! Margaret!

Come, dear children, come away down;
Call no more!
One last look at the white-wall'd town,
And the little grey church on the windy shore;
Then come down!

She will not come though you call all day;
Come away, come away!

Children dear, was it yesterday
We heard the sweet bells over the bay?
In the caverns where we lay,
Through the surf and through the swell,
The far-off sound of a silver bell?

Sand-strewn caverns, cool and deep,
Where the winds are all asleep;
Where the spent lights quiver and gleam,
Where the salt weed sways in the stream,
Where the sea-beasts, ranged all round,
Feed in the ooze of their pasture-ground;
Where the sea-snakes coil and twine,
Dry their mail and bask in the brine;
Where great whales come sailing by,
Sail and sail, with unshut eye,
Round the world for ever and aye?
When did music come this way?
Children dear, was it yesterday?

Children dear, was it yesterday
(Call yet once) that she went away?
Once she sate with you and me,
On a red gold throne in the heart of the sea,
And the youngest sate on her knee.
She comb'd its bright hair, and she tended it well,
When down swung the sound of a far-off bell.
She sigh'd, she look'd up though the clear green sea.
She said: 'I must go, for my kinsfolk pray
In the little grey church on the shore to-day.

'Twill be Easter-time in the world – ah me!
And I lose my poor soul, Merman! here with thee.'
I said: 'Go up, dear heart, through the waves;
Say thy prayer, and come back to the kind sea-caves!'
She smiled, she went up through the surf in the bay.
Children dear, was it yesterday?

Children dear, were we long alone?
'The sea grows stormy, the little ones moan;
Long prayers,' I said, 'in the world they say;
Come!' I said; and we rose through the surf in the bay.
We went up the beach, by the sandy down
Where the sea-stocks bloom, to the white-wall'd town.
Through the narrow paved streets, where all was still.
To the little grey church on the windy hill.

From the church came a murmur of folk at their prayers,
But we stood without in the cold blowing airs.
We climb'd on the graves, on the stones worn with rains,
And we gazed up the aisle through the small leaded panes.
She sate by the pillar; we saw her clear:
'Margaret, hist! come quick, we are here!
Dear heart,' I said, 'we are long alone;
The sea grows stormy, the little ones moan.'
But, ah, she gave me never a look,
For her eyes were seal'd to the holy book!
Loud prays the priest; shut stands the door.
Come away, children, call no more!
Come away, come down, call no more!

Down, down, down!
Down to the depths of the sea!
She sits at her wheel in the humming town,

Singing most joyfully.
Hark what she sings: 'O joy, O joy,
For the humming street, and the child with its toy!
For the priest, and the bell, and the holy well;
For the wheel where I spun,
And the blessed light of the sun!'
And so she sings her fill,
Singing most joyfully,
Till the spindle drops from her hand,
And the whizzing wheel stands still.
She steals to the window, and looks at the sand,
And over the sand at the sea;
And her eyes are set in a stare;
And anon there breaks a sigh,
And anon there drops a tear,
From a sorrow-clouded eye,
And a heart sorrow-laden,
A long, long sigh;
For the cold strange eyes of a little Mermaiden
And the gleam of her golden hair.

Come away, away children;
Come children, come down!
The hoarse wind blows coldly;
Lights shine in the town.
She will start from her slumber
When gusts shake the door;
She will hear the winds howling,
Will hear the waves roar.
We shall see, while above us
The waves roar and whirl,
A ceiling of amber,

A pavement of pearl.
Singing: 'Here came a mortal,
But faithless was she!
And alone dwell for ever
The kings of the sea.'

But, children, at midnight,
When soft the winds blow,
When clear falls the moonlight,
When spring-tides are low;
When sweet airs come seaward
From heaths starr'd with broom,
And high rocks throw mildly
On the blanch'd sands a gloom;
Up the still, glistening beaches,
Up the creeks we will hie,
Over banks of bright seaweed
The ebb-tide leaves dry.
We will gaze, from the sand-hills,
At the white, sleeping town;
At the church on the hill-side –
And then come back down.
Singing: 'There dwells a loved one,
But cruel is she!
She left lonely for ever
The kings of the sea.'

Matthew Arnold

The Lion and Albert

There's a famous seaside place called Blackpool,
That's noted for fresh air and fun,
And Mr and Mrs Ramsbottom
Went there with young Albert, their son.

A grand little lad was young Albert,
All dressed in his best; quite a swell
With a stick and an 'orse's 'ead 'andle,
The finest that Woolworth's could sell.

They didn't think much to the Ocean:
The waves, they was fiddlin' and small,
There was no wrecks and nobody drownded,
Fact, nothing to laugh at at all.

So, seeking for further amusement,
They paid and went into the Zoo,
Where they'd Lions and Tigers and Camels,
And old ale and sandwiches too.

There was one great big Lion called Wallace;
His nose were all covered with scars –
He lay in a somnolent posture
With the side of his face on the bars.

Now Albert had heard about lions,
How they was ferocious and wild –
To see Wallace lying so peaceful,
Well, it didn't seem right to the child.

So straightway the brave little feller,
Not showing a morsel of fear,
Took his stick with its 'orse's 'ead 'andle
And pushed it in Wallace's ear.

You could see that the lion didn't like it,
For giving a kind of a roll,
He pulled Albert inside the cage with 'im
And swallowed the little lad 'ole.

Then Pa, who had seen the occurrence,
And didn't know what to do next,
Said 'Mother! Yon Lion's 'et Albert,'
And Mother said 'Well, I am vexed!'

Then Mr and Mrs Ramsbottom –
Quite rightly, when all's said and done –
Complained to the Animal Keeper
That the Lion had eaten their son.

The keeper was quite nice about it;
He said 'What a nasty mishap.
Are you sure that it's *your* boy he's eaten?'
Pa said 'Am I sure? There's his cap!'

The manager had to be sent for.
He came and he said 'What's to do?'
Pa said 'Yon Lion's 'et Albert,
And 'im in his Sunday clothes, too.'

Then Mother said, 'Right's right, young feller;
I think it's a shame and a sin
For a lion to go and eat Albert,
And after we've paid to come in.'

The manager wanted no trouble,
He took out his purse right away,
Saying 'How much to settle the matter?'
And Pa said 'What do you usually pay?'

But Mother had turned a bit awkward
When she thought where her Albert had gone.
She said 'No! someone's got to be summonsed' –
So that was decided upon.

Then off they went to the P'lice Station,
In front of the Magistrate chap;
They told 'im what happened to Albert,
And proved it by showing his cap.

The Magistrate gave his opinion
That no one was really to blame
And he said that he hoped the Ramsbottoms
Would have further sons to their name.

At that Mother got proper blazing,
'And thank you, sir, kindly,' said she.
'What, waste all our lives raising children
To feed ruddy Lions? Not me!'

Marriott Edgar

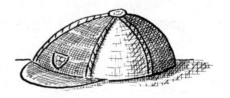

Count Carrots

A small wind lightly
steps over the harebells…

Like tall ragged kings
rise the fir trees of Bohemia…

And I remember too
the scarlet and purple berries…

He's the giant of the mountains;
they call him Count Carrots.
How he hates that nickname.
Let me tell you how he came by it.

Well – there was that princess
who – Persephone-like –
had strayed from her companions.
Perhaps you know the story.

It was all meadows and summer.
It was harebells and clover.
It was tall marguerites.
It was field flowers thousands and thousands,

or so it seemed.
The princess
was tempted to pick the best posy of all.
She ran this way and that, further and further away.

And the voices behind her grew fainter,
and the sky above her grew bluer,

and the sweet meadow engulfed her.
And suddenly – vast arms lifted her into the air.

The princess screamed. Or she may have fainted.
Then the giant of the mountain lifted her onto his
                                                shoulders.
He was swarthy and hairy; he was gnarled and muscled
                                                like trees.
His stride was long. The princess vanished from sight.

What had her companions been doing?
Asking the daisies who loved them.
Putting buttercups under each other's chin.
'If it shows gold in reflection, it means you like butter.'

Only later they missed her.
The consternation of it;
the runnings to and fro;
the calling, over and over.

'What shall we tell them at home?'
And who will comfort ever
the queen in tears,
the king in despair?

There was one other who heard the news
of the disappearance. He was the prince
whom the princess loved.
He saddled his horse and set out in search of her.

As for the giant, he carried the princess
to his cave under the mountains.
Some say he brought her gifts of precious stones
to tempt her to love him. This is untrue,

he was simpler than that. He brought her, I think,
bilberries from the forest, baskets of raspberries,
mushrooms, many sorts, which Bohemia excels in,
and clumsy importunings, day after day.

He brought her wild strawberries, gathered from steep
hills.
She was used to sugar and cream; she was used to pretty
bowls
from which to eat them. He roasted venison: the smoke
stung her eyes, she said. She feared the spluttering fat.

The fact is – to paddle your feet in a mountain stream,
shallow and fast and cold as molten ice, water which
rushes and swirls
over white pebbles, – to paddle your feet in this on a hot
day
is pleasant and delightful: to wash in it, day after day,

indubitably cold. So the princess had discovered.
Besides, she missed her companions, she missed the
court and the fun.
She missed, of course, her mother and father, she said.
She missed her little dog, Peep. And she missed her
prince.

'Ah, giant, you brought me here against my inclinations.
I am not made for this rocky existence.
Forests are well enough for Sunday hikes.
My dog, Peep, would enjoy them.' Here her tears rolled
down.

The giant, slow and ponderous, then had an idea,
which he should have thought of before.
He had some magic. He had a field of carrots.
He brought some to the princess. 'These carrots,' he said,

'can be changed, as you will, by magic into whomever,
whatever, you wish, say, your dog, Peep.'
So the princess wished, and one of the carrots
became her little dog. There he stood, yapping.

The princess, laughing in pleasure and disbelief,
stroked him and patted him and took him into her arms,
then put him down again; the little carrot dog
wagged his tail and sniffed at the venison. He was as like
                                                    as like.

Then the princess went to work and said to one carrot:
'You'll be friend Sylvia.' And there Sylvia stood,
and laughed and embraced her, and was no carrot at all.
And so: 'You shall be Alice, you shall be John.'

Then the carrots were turned into friends and footmen,
chambermaids, courtiers, horses to ride on, by the
                                                    princess, –
even goblets to drink from. Ah, but she had a good time.
She was gracious to the giant. She didn't see much of him.

She had a proper court. It was almost like home.
They went riding at dawn. In the evening they danced.
Then on the third morning, or was it the fourth?
her horse as she rode him began somewhat to droop.

A fine chestnut he was. What could be up with him?
He could hardly manage it back to the caves;
his step stumbling, his very flesh shrunken.
The princess was anxious and looked around for help.

'Sylvia,' she cried to her friend, the groom not being
                                                    around.
But Sylvia too looked pale and complained of her head.
Something was wrong with Sylvia… Something was
                                                very wrong!
The groom she had called for lay in a ditch, dead,

and suddenly turned back into a carrot again.
Yes, carrots shrivel when out of the ground, and so
one by one as the carrots died so did her friends
shrivel and turn into carrots again – the magic gone.

That night at dinner only one servant was left to
pour out her wine. As he poured, he bent at the waist
more than he should. He drooped and tottered off;
and the stem of the wine-glass bent too. The wine spilt red.

Her face full of shock and woe, the princess went to the
                                                    giant,
who looked guilty and sorry. But then he said:
'Darling princess, the fields are full of carrots.
I can bring you carrots freshly each day, to replace those
                                                    lost.'

Well, so he did, but the princess felt uneasy;
until she hit on a cunning plan. 'Giant,' she pleaded,
'I fear you may one day run out of carrots. Count them
                                                    for me
to see how many there are.' – So he did: one by one.

That would take him a day and a bit. His back was
                                                    turned,
and he bent over the furrows with furrowed brow.
Then the princess picked some carrots, the freshest,
                                        the strongest,
and turned two into horses, and one into the prince,

the semblance of him whom she loved.
They rode away with the speed of a wish,
through forests of pine,
through thickets, past mountain streams,

into the valley below.
(Do not fear, do not falter,
do not yet fall behind.
Good Hope, stay by my side.)

So the princess prayed.
And they are fortunate
whom a vision of love
accompanies.

Meanwhile what of the giant?
Ah, but that booby
was still counting his carrots:
'Five-hundred… six-hundred…
                        six-hundred-and-seventy-two…

Did he try to pursue her?
The story says he did.
Surely, he lumbered one day out of the forest,
to knock her up, knock her down, rap for some reply…

And no reply ever: the castle ears
closed tight to his bellowing lungs; the castle gates
forever shut to him; the curtains too,
though he reached to the topmost storey, drawn to his
                                                    gaze.

Into the sulky night he plodded like thunder,
and the small pillow, rosy in lamplight, whispered
to the burly wind beating against the door:
'You will never bluster your way into *my* down.'

Henceforth, the giant was called Count Carrots by all;
a nickname he hates, as I told you at the beginning.
Woe to him who so calls him in mischief. Let the
impudent traveller, shouting his name, beware.

When I was small, I called his name to the forest:
'Count Carrots! Count Carrots!' then leapt into bed,
                                                half in fear.
He didn't come for me though. Could it be that perhaps
                                                he forgave me?
He loves children, they say. – May the forest stay green
                                                for him ever.

Gerda Mayer
(from a Bohemian folk-tale called *Rübezahl*)

The Sands of Dee

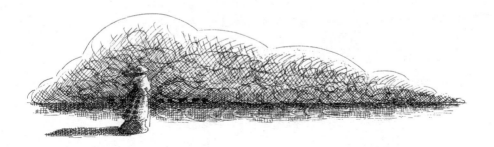

'O Mary, go and call the cattle home,
        And call the cattle home,
        And call the cattle home,
     Across the sands of Dee';
The western wind was wild and dank with foam,
      And all alone went she.

The western tide crept up along the sand,
        And o'er and o'er the sand,
        And round and round the sand,
     As far as eye could see.
The rolling mist came down and hid the land:
      And never home came she.

'O is it weed, or fish, or floating hair –
        A tress of golden hair,
        A drownèd maiden's hair,
    Above the nets at sea?'
Was never salmon yet that shone so fair
    Among the stakes of Dee.

They rowed her in across the rolling foam,
        The cruel crawling foam,
        The cruel hungry foam,
    To her grave beside the sea:
But still the boatmen hear her call the cattle home
    Across the sands of Dee.

Charles Kingsley

The Lady of Shalott

PART I

On either side the river lie
Long fields of barley and of rye,
That clothe the wold and meet the sky;
And thro' the field the road runs by
    To many tower'd Camelot;
And up and down the people go,
Gazing where the lilies blow
Round an island there below,
    The island of Shalott.

Willows whiten, aspens quiver,
Little breezes dusk and shiver
Thro' the wave that runs for ever
By the island in the river
    Flowing down to Camelot.
Four gray walls, and four gray towers,
Overlook a space of flowers,
And the silent isle imbowers
    The Lady of Shalott.

By the margin, willow-veil'd,
Slide the heavy barges trail'd
By slow horses; and unhail'd
The shallop flitteth silken-sail'd
    Skimming down to Camelot:
But who hath seen her wave her hand?
Or at the casement seen her stand?
Or is she known in all the land,
    The Lady of Shalott?

Only reapers, reaping early
In among the bearded barley,
Hear a song that echoes cheerly
From the river winding clearly
    Down to tower'd Camelot:
And by the moon the reaper weary,
Piling sheaves in uplands airy,
Listening, whispers ''Tis the fairy
    Lady of Shalott.'

PART II

There she weaves by night and day
A magic web with colours gay.
She has heard a whisper say,
A curse is on her if she stay
    To look down to Camelot.
She knows not what the curse may be,
And so she weaveth steadily,
And little other care hath she,
    The Lady of Shalott.

And moving thro' a mirror clear
That hangs before her all the year,
Shadows of the world appear.
There she sees the highway near
    Winding down to Camelot:
There the river eddy whirls,
And there the surly village-churls,
And the red cloaks of market girls,
    Pass onward from Shalott.

Sometimes a troop of damsels glad,
An abbot on an ambling pad,

Sometimes a curly shepherd-lad,
Or long-hair'd page in crimson clad,
    Goes by to tower'd Camelot;
And sometimes thro' the mirror blue
The knights come riding two and two:
She hath no loyal knight and true,
    The Lady of Shalott.

But in her web she still delights
To weave the mirror's magic sights,
For often thro' the silent nights
A funeral, with plumes and lights,
    And music, went to Camelot;
Or when the moon was overhead,
Came two young lovers lately wed;
'I am half sick of shadows,' said
    The Lady of Shalott.

PART III

A bow-shot from her bower-eaves,
He rode between the barley-sheaves,
The sun came dazzling thro' the leaves,
And flamed upon the brazen greaves
    Of bold Sir Lancelot.
A red-cross knight for ever kneel'd
To a lady in his shield,
That sparkled on the yellow field,
    Beside remote Shalott.

The gemmy bridle glitter'd free,
Like to some branch of stars we see
Hung in the golden Galaxy.
The bridle bells rang merrily

As he rode down to Camelot:
And from his blazon'd baldric slung
A mighty silver bugle hung,
And as he rode his armour rung,
    Beside remote Shalott.

All in the blue unclouded weather
Thick-jewell'd shone the saddle-leather,
The helmet and the helmet-feather
Burn'd like one burning flame together,
    As he rode down to Camelot.
As often thro' the purple night,
Below the starry clusters bright,
Some bearded meteor, trailing light,
    Moves over still Shalott.

His broad clear brow in sunlight glow'd;
On burnish'd hooves his war-horse trode;
From underneath his helmet flow'd
His coal-black curls as on he rode,
    As he rode down to Camelot.
From the bank and from the river
He flash'd into the crystal mirror,
'Tirra lirra,' by the river
    Sang Sir Lancelot.

She left the web, she left the loom,
She made three paces thro' the room,
She saw the water-lily bloom,
She saw the helmet and the plume,
    She look'd down to Camelot.
Out flew the web and floated wide;
The mirror crack'd from side to side;

'The curse is come upon me!' cried
    The Lady of Shalott.

PART IV

In the stormy east-wind straining,
The pale yellow woods were waning,
The broad stream in his banks complaining,
Heavily the low sky raining
    Over tower'd Camelot;
Down she came and found a boat
Beneath a willow left afloat,
And round about the prow she wrote
    The Lady of Shalott.

And down the river's dim expanse –
Like some bold seer in a trance,
Seeing all his own mischance –
With a glassy countenance
    Did she look to Camelot.
And at the closing of the day
She loosed her chain, and down she lay;
The broad stream bore her far away,
    The Lady of Shalott.

Lying, robed in snowy white
That loosely flew to left and right –
The leaves upon her falling light –
Thro' the noises of the night
    She floated down to Camelot;
And as the boat-head wound along
The willowy hills and fields among,
They heard her singing her last song,
    The Lady of Shalott.

Heard a carol, mournful, holy,
Chanted loudly, chanted lowly,
Till her blood was frozen slowly,
And her eyes were darken'd wholly,
    Turn'd to tower'd Camelot;
For ere she reach'd upon the tide
The first house by the water-side,
Singing in her song she died,
    The Lady of Shalott.

Under tower and balcony,
By garden-wall and gallery,
A gleaming shape she floated by,
Dead-pale between the houses high,
    Silent into Camelot.
Out upon the wharfs they came,
Knight and burgher, lord and dame,
And round the prow they read her name,
    The Lady of Shalott.

Who is this? and what is here?
And in the lighted palace near
Died the sound of royal cheer;
And they cross'd themselves for fear,
    All the knights at Camelot:
But Lancelot mused a little space;
He said, 'She has a lovely face;
God in His mercy lend her grace,
    The Lady of Shalott.'

Alfred, Lord Tennyson

The Listeners

'Is there anybody there?' said the Traveller,
    Knocking on the moonlit door;
And his horse in the silence champed the grasses
    Of the forest's ferny floor:
And a bird flew up out of the turret,
    Above the Traveller's head:
And he smote upon the door again a second time;
    'Is there anybody there?' he said.
But no one descended to the Traveller;
    No head from the leaf-fringed sill
Leaned over and looked into his grey eyes,
    Where he stood perplexed and still.
But only a host of phantom listeners
    That dwelt in the lone house then
Stood listening in the quiet of the moonlight
    To that voice from the world of men:
Stood thronging the faint moonbeams on the dark stair,
    That goes down to the empty hall,
Hearkening in an air stirred and shaken
    By the lonely Traveller's call.
And he felt in his heart their strangeness,
    Their stillness answering his cry,
While his horse moved, cropping the dark turf,
    'Neath the starred and leafy sky;
For he suddenly smote on the door, even
    Louder, and lifted his head:–
'Tell them I came, and no one answered,
    That I kept my word,' he said.

Never the least stir made the listeners,
    Though every word he spake
Fell echoing through the shadowiness of the still house
    From the one man left awake:
Ay, they heard his foot upon the stirrup,
    And the sound of iron on stone,
And how the silence surged softly backward,
    When the plunging hoofs were gone.

Walter de la Mare

The Burglar

When the burglar went out
to burgle a house

When the burglar pulled on
his black polo-neck,
his beret, his Reeboks

When the burglar rattled
his skeleton keys,
checked he had his street-map,
said goodbye to his budgie

When the burglar shouldered
an empty bag, big enough
to take as much swag
as the burglar could carry

When the burglar waited
for the bus

When the burglar stood
at the bottom of the street
where the house he'd picked
to burgle was

When the burglar burgled
he didn't know
that another burglar
was inside *his* house

And only the budgie would see

Matthew Sweeney

Robin Hood and Alan a Dale

I

Come listen to me, you gallants so free
    All you that love mirth for to hear,
And I will tell you of a bold outlaw,
    That lived in Nottinghamshire.

II

As Robin Hood in the forest stood,
    All under the green-wood tree,
There he was ware of a brave young man,
    As fine as fine might be.

III

The youngster was clothed in scarlet red,
    In scarlet fine and gay,
And he did frisk it over the plain,
    And chanted a roundelay.

IV

As Robin Hood next morning stood,
    Amongst the leaves so gay,
There did he espy the same young man
    Come drooping along the way.

V

The scarlet he wore the day before,
    It was clean cast away;
And every step he fetcht a sigh,
    'Alack and well a day!'

Then steppèd forth brave Little John,
    And Much the miller's son,
Which made the young man bend his bow,
    When as he saw them come.

'Stand off, stand off!' the young man said,
    'What is your will with me?' –
'You must come before our master straight,
    Under yon green-wood tree.'

And when he came bold Robin before,
    Robin asked him courteously,
'O hast thou any money to spare,
    For my merry men and me?'

'I have no money,' the young man said,
    'But five shillings and a ring;
And that I have kept this seven long years,
    To have it at my wedding.

'Yesterday I should have married a maid,
    But she from me is tane,
And chosen to be an old knight's delight,
    Whereby my poor heart is slain.'

'What is thy name?' then said Robin Hood,
    'Come tell me, without any fail.'–

'By the faith of my body,' then said the young man,
  'My name it is Alan a Dale.'

XII

'What wilt thou give me,' said Robin Hood,
  'In ready gold or fee,
To help thee to thy true-love again,
  And deliver her unto thee?'

XIII

'I have no money,' then quoth the young man,
  'No ready gold nor fee,
But I will swear upon a book
  Thy true servant for to be.' –

XIV

'How many miles is it to thy true-love?
  Come tell me without guile.' –
'By the faith of my body,' then said the young man,
  'It is but five little mile.'

XV

Then Robin he hasted over the plain,
  He did neither stint nor lin,
Until he came unto the church
  Where Alan should keep his wedding.

XVI

'What hast thou here?' the Bishop he said,
  'I prithee now tell unto me':
'I am a bold harper,' quoth Robin Hood,
  'And the best in the north countrey.'

39

'O welcome, O welcome!' the Bishop he said,
  'That musick best pleaseth me.'–
'You shall have no musick,' quoth Robin Hood,
  'Till the bride and the bridegroom I see.'

XVIII

With that came in a wealthy knight,
  Which was both grave and old,
And after him a finikin lass,
  Did shine like the glistering gold.

XIX

'This is no fit match,'quoth bold Robin Hood,
  'That you do seem to make here;
For since we are come into the church,
  The bride she shall choose her own dear.'

XX

Then Robin Hood put his horn to his mouth,
  And blew blasts two or three;
When four and twenty bowmen bold
  Come leaping over the lee.

XXI

And when they came into the churchyard,
  Marching all on a row,
The first man was Alan a Dale
  To give bold Robin his bow.

XXII

'This is thy true-love,' Robin he said,
  'Young Alan, as I hear say;

And you shall be married at this same time,
    Before we depart away.'

XXIII

'That shall not be,' the Bishop he said,
    'For thy word shall not stand;
They shall be three times asked in the church,
    As the law is of our land.'

XXIV

Robin Hood pull'd off the Bishop's coat,
    And put it upon Little John;
'By the faith of my body,' then Robin said,
    'This cloth doth make thee a man.'

XXV

When Little John went into the quire,
    The people began to laugh;
He asked them seven times in the church,
    Least three times should not be enough.

XXVI

'Who gives me this maid?' said Little John;
    Quoth Robin Hood, 'That do I!
And he that takes her from Alan a Dale
    Full dearly he shall her buy.'

XXVII

And thus having ended this merry wedding,
    The bride looked like a queen,
And so they return'd to the merry green-wood,
    Amongst the leaves so green.

Anon

The Silkie of Sule Skerry

An earthly nurse, she sits and sings
And aye she sings, by lily, by wean
Tis little ken I my bairn's father
Nor yet the land where he dwells in.

He came one night to my bed's feet
And a grimly guest, I'm sure was he
Saying 'Here am I, thy bairn's father
Although I be not comely.

'I am a man upon the land
I am a silkie on the sea
And when I'm far and far from land
My home it is the sule skerry.'

And he hath ta'en a purse of gold
And he hath placed it on her knee
Saying 'Give to me my little young son
And take thee up thy nurse's fee.

'It shall come to pass, one summer's day,
When the sun shines bright on every stone
I'll come and fetch my little young son
And teach him how to swim the foam.

'And you shall marry a gunner bold
A gunner bold I'm sure he'll be
And the very first shot that he will shoot
Will kill both my young son and me.'

And it came to pass one summer's day
When the sun shone bright across the sea
That the very first shot of that gunner bold
Did kill the seals of Sule Skerry.

'I am a man upon the land
I am a silkie on the sea
And when I'm far and far from land
My home it is the sule skerry.'

Traditional

Overheard in County Sligo

I married a man from County Roscommon
and I live at the back of beyond
with a field of cows and a yard of hens
and six white geese on the pond.

At my door's a square of yellow corn
caught up by its corners and shaken,
and the road runs down through the open gate
and freedom's there for the taking.

I had thought to work on the Abbey stage
or have my name in a book,
to see my thought on the printed page,
or still the crowd with a look.

But I turn to fold the breakfast cloth
and to polish the lustre and brass,
to order and dust the tumbled rooms
and find my face in the glass.

I ought to feel I'm a happy woman
for I lie in the lap of the land,
and I married a man from County Roscommon
and I live in the back of beyond.

Gillian Clarke

The Bandoline Player

A troubadour, young, brave, and tall,
    One morning might be seen,
A singing under Colter's hall
    Upon the village green.

He went through all the usual forms,
    And rolled his eyes of blue,
As dying ducks in thunderstorms
    Are often said to do.

For Colter had a daughter, she
    Was barely twenty-two.
Why sang that minstrel party? He
    Adored her – so would you.

He played upon a what's-its-name –
    You know the thing I mean –
The *Pall Mall* critics call the same
    A 'dainty bandoline.'

And Colter's daughter, wrapt in joy
    (A sweet, romantic maid),
She smiled upon that guileless boy
    As gracefully he played.

'Oh person in the crimson legs,'
    She modestly exclaimed,
'A bashful maiden coyly begs
    You'll tell her how you're named.

'For, oh, you feed a tender flame
    In playing on the green,
And, oh she loves what critics name
    The dainty bandoline!'

That troubadour he tore his hair
    And sent a sigh above,
To think his bandoline should share
    That maiden's wealth of love.

He hied him to his village shed,
    Wept village tears in quarts,
Then laid him on his village bed,
    And thought these village thoughts:

'I must be worshipped all in all –
    For what I've always been –
And not for what the critics call
    My dainty bandoline.

'To which of us her loving may
    Be due, I'll thus detect –
Upon the fiddle I can play
    With singular effect.

'To-morrow, with its graceful aid,
    Her moments I'll beguile,
That maiden I will serenade
    In Joachim's finest style.'

And so he did, that gallant boy,
    But never came the maid;
He, hoping she was only coy,
    Still sang to her and played.

Beethoven, Gluck, Piccinni, Spohr –
    He gave her for a while:
And other masters, even more,
    'Dot-touch-and-go' in style.

For hours that patient boy he played
    At Father Colter's farm –
Behind his noble shoulder-blade,
    And underneath his arm –

Below his leg – behind his back –
    He played till he was red –
Between his knees, with dainty knack,
    And then above his head.

With musico-gymnastic tricks
    He warbled forth her name;
From half-past nine till half-past six,
    But, ah! no maiden came.

(For Mary had been sent away
    To Weston-super-Mare –
A fact of which that minstrel gay
    Was wholly unware.)

But Father Colter rose at nine,
    His wrath it also rised,
For fiddle, voice, and bandoline
    He equally despised.

'I have,' said he, 'some bellows *here* –
    A fine young noddle *there* –
It would but be politeness mere
    To introduce the pair!'

No sooner was it said than done,
    And as above I've shown,
Upon the sconce he fetched him one –
    One for himself alone!

'Ah, Mary,' said the simple lad,
    'I know thy gentle touch.
Upon my word this is too bad,
    I feel it very much.

'That you don't care for me at all
    Is easy to be seen –
You love what *Pall Mall* critics call
    My dainty bandoline.'

(But Mary had been sent away
    To Weston-super-Mare –
A fact of which that minstrel gay
    Was wholly unaware.)

W S Gilbert

The Owl and the Pussy-Cat

The Owl and the Pussy-Cat went to sea
In a beautiful pea-green boat.
They took some honey, and plenty of money,
Wrapped up in a five-pound note.
The Owl looked up to the stars above,
And sang to a small guitar,
'O lovely Pussy! O Pussy, my love,
What a beautiful Pussy you are,
You are!
What a beautiful Pussy you are!'

Pussy said to the Owl, 'You elegant fowl,
How charmingly sweet you sing!
Oh! Let us be married! Too long we have tarried:
But what shall we do for a ring?'
They sailed away for a year and a day,
To the land where the Bong-tree grows;
And there in the wood a Piggy-wig stood,
With a ring at the end of his nose,
His nose,
With a ring at the end of his nose.

'Dear Pig, are you willing to sell for one shilling
Your ring?' Said the Piggy, 'I will.'
So they took it away, and were married next day
By the Turkey who lives on the hill.
They dined on mince, and slices of quince,
Which they ate with a runcible spoon;
And hand in hand, on the edge of the sand,
They danced by the light of the moon,
The moon,
They danced by the light of the moon.

Edward Lear

Mart

Mart was my best friend.
I thought he was great,
but one day he tried to do for me.

I had a hat – a woolly one
and I loved that hat.
It was warm and tight.
My mum had knitted it
and I wore it everywhere.

One day me and Mart were out
and we were standing at a bus-stop
and suddenly
he goes and grabs my hat
and chucked it over the wall.
He thought I was going to go in there
and get it out.
He thought he'd make me do that
because he knew I liked that hat so much
I wouldn't be able to stand being without it.

He was right –
I could hardly bear it.
I was really scared I'd never get it back.
But I never let on.
I never showed it on my face.
I just waited.

'Aren't you going to get your hat?'
he says.
'Your hat's gone,' he says.
'Your hat's over the wall.'
I looked the other way.

But I could still feel on my head
how he had pulled it off.
'Your hat's over the wall,' he says.
I didn't say a thing.

Then the bus came round the corner
at the end of the road.

If I go home without my hat
I'm going to walk through the door
and Mum's going to say,
'Where's your hat?'
and if I say,
'It's over the wall,'
she's going to say,
'What's it doing there?'
and I'm going to say,
'Mart chucked it over,'
and she's going to say,
'Why didn't you go for it?'
and what am I going to say then?
What am I going to say then?

The bus was coming up.
'Aren't you going over for your hat?
There won't be another bus for ages,'
Mart says.

The bus was coming closer.
'You've lost your hat now,'
Mart says.

The bus stopped.
I got on
Mart got on
The bus moved off.

'You've lost your hat,' Mart says.

'You've lost your hat,' Mart says.

Two stops ahead, was ours.
'Are you going indoors without it?' Mart says.
I didn't say a thing.

The bus stopped.

Mart got up
and dashed downstairs.
He'd got off one stop early.
I got off when we got to our stop.

I went home
walked through the door
'Where's your hat?' Mum says.
'Over a wall,' I said.
'What's it doing there?' she says.
'Mart chucked it over there,' I said.
'But you haven't left it there, have you?' she says.
'Yes,' I said.

'Well don't you ever come asking me to make you
anything like that again.
You make me tired, you do.'

Later,
I was drinking some orange juice.
The front door-bell rang.
It was Mart.
He had the hat in his hand.
He handed it to me – and went.

I shut the front door –
put on the hat
and walked into the kitchen.
Mum looked up.
'You don't need to wear your hat indoors do you?'
she said.
'I will for a bit,' I said.
And I did.

Michael Rosen

Legend

The blacksmith's boy went out with a rifle
and a black dog running behind.
Cobwebs snatched at his feet,
rivers hindered him,
thorn-branches caught at his eyes to make him blind
and the sky turned into an unlucky opal,
but he didn't mind,
I can break branches, I can swim rivers, I can stare
                       out any spider I meet,
said he to his dog and his rifle.

The blacksmith's boy went over the paddocks
with his old black hat on his head.
Mountains jumped in his way,
rocks rolled down on him,
and the old crow cried, 'You'll soon be dead.'
And the rain came down like mattocks.
But he only said
I can climb mountains, I can dodge rocks, I can shoot
                       an old crow any day,
and he went on over the paddocks.

When he came to the end of the day the sun began
                             falling.
Up came the night ready to swallow him,
like the barrel of a gun,
like an old black hat,
like a black dog hungry to follow him.

Then the pigeon, the magpie and the dove began wailing
and the grass lay down to pillow him.
His rifle broke, his hat blew away and his dog was gone
and the sun was falling.

But in front of the night the rainbow stood on the
                                        mountain,
just as his heart foretold.
He ran like a hare,
he climbed like a fox;
he caught it in his hands, the colours and the cold –
like a bar of ice, like the column of a fountain,
like a ring of gold.
The pigeon, the magpie and the dove flew up to stare,
and the grass stood up again on the mountain.

The blacksmith's boy hung the rainbow on his shoulder
instead of his broken gun.
Lizards ran out to see,
snakes made way for him,
and the rainbow shone as brightly as the sun.
All the world said, Nobody is braver, nobody is bolder,
nobody else has done
anything to equal it. He went home as bold as he
                                        could be
with the swinging rainbow on his shoulder.

Judith Wright

The Red Headed Ann

The wee birds were lining the bleak Autumn branches,
Just preparing to fly to a far sunny shore
When the tinkers made camp at a bend in the river,
Coming back from the horse-fair at Ballaghisheon.

Now the harvest being over, the farmer came walking
All along the fair river that borders his land
And twas there he first saw her twixt firelight and water,
The tinkerman's daughter, the red headed Ann.

Now next morning he rose from a night without resting,
He went straight to her father and he made his case
known
And in a pub in Listowel they worked out a bargain,
For the tinker a pony and for his daughter a home.

Where the trees spread their shadows along the fair river
The tinker and farmer inspected the land
And a white gelding pony was the price they agreed on
For the tinkerman's daughter, the red headed Ann.

Now the wedding soon over the tinkers departed.
They were eager to travel on south down the road
But the crunch of the iron shod wheels on the ground
Was as bitter to her as the way she'd been sold.

But she tried hard to please him, she did all his bidding,
For she slept in his bed and she worked on his land,
But the walls of that cabin pressed tighter and tighter
On that tinkerman's daughter, the red headed Ann.

Now as white as the hands of the priest or the hangman,
The snow spread its blanket the next Christmas round
And the tinkerman's daughter she slipped out from his
                                                bedside.
She turned her back on the land and her face to the town.

Yes it's said someone saw her at dusk the same evening
As she was making her way out past Lireconpon,
Aye and that was the last time the settled folk saw her,
The tinkerman's daughter, the red headed Ann.

Where the North Kerry hills cuts the Feale near
                                                Listowel,
At a farm on its banks lives a bitter old man
And he swears by the shotgun that he keeps by his
                                                bedside
That he'll kill any tinker that camps on his land.

Yet whenever he hears iron shod wheels crunch on gravel
Or a horse in the shafts of a bright caravan,
Then his day's work's tormented, his night's sleep's
                                                demented,
By the tinkerman's daughter, the red headed Ann.

Micky McConnell

Mountain Lion

Climbing through the January snow, into the
                              Lobo Canyon
Dark grow the spruce-trees, blue is the balsam,
          water sounds still unfrozen, and the trail is still
                              evident.

Men!
Two men!
Men! The only animal in the world to fear!

They hesitate.
We hesitate.
They have a gun.
We have no gun.

Then we all advance, to meet.

Two Mexicans, strangers, emerging out of the
     dark and snow and inwardness of the Lobo valley.
     What are they doing here on this vanishing trail?

What is he carrying?
Something yellow.
A deer?

Qué tiene, amigo?
León –

He smiles, foolishly, as if he were caught doing wrong.
And we smile, foolishly, as if we didn't know.
He is quite gentle and dark-faced.

It is a mountain lion,
A long, long slim cat, yellow like a lioness.
Dead.

He trapped her this morning, he says, smiling foolishly.
Lift up her face,
Her round, bright face, bright as frost.
Her round, fine-fashioned head, with two dead ears;
And stripes in the brilliant frost of her face,
                                    sharp, fine dark rays,
Dark, keen, fine rays in the brilliant frost of her face.
Beautiful dead eyes.

Hermoso es!

They go out towards the open;
We go on into the gloom of Lobo.
And above the trees I found her lair,
A hole in the blood-orange brilliant rocks that
                                    stick up, a little cave.
And bones, and twigs, and a perilous ascent.

So, she will never leap up that way again, with
                    the yellow flash of a mountain lion's long
                                                    shoot!
And her bright striped frost-face will never watch
                any more, out of the shadow of the cave in the
                                        blood-orange rock,
Above the trees of the Lobo dark valley-mouth!

Instead, I look out.
And out to the dim of the desert, like a dream,
                                    never real;
To the snow of the Sangre de Cristo mountains,
     the ice of the mountains of Picoris,
And near across at the opposite steep of snow,
     green trees motionless standing in snow, like a
                                    Christmas toy.

And I think in this empty world there was room
     for me and a mountain lion.
And I think in the world beyond, how easily we
     might spare a million or two of humans
And never miss them.
Yet what a gap in the world, the missing white
     frost-face of that slim yellow mountain lion!

D H Lawrence

Jabberwocky

'Twas brillig, and the slithy toves
    Did gyre and gimble in the wabe:
All mimsy were the borogoves,
    And the mome raths outgrabe.

'Beware the Jabberwock, my son!
    The jaws that bite, the claws that catch!
Beware the Jubjub bird, and shun
    The frumious Bandersnatch!'

He took his vorpal sword in hand:
    Long time the manxome foe he sought –
So rested he by the Tumtum tree,
    And stood awhile in thought.

And, as in uffish thought he stood,
    The Jabberwock, with eyes of flame,
Came whiffling through the tulgey wood,
    And burbled as it came!

One, two! One, two! And through and through
    The vorpal blade went snicker-snack!
He left it dead, and with its head
    He went galumphing back.

'And hast thou slain the Jabberwock?
    Come to my arms, my beamish boy!
O frabjous day! Callooh! Callay!'
    He chortled in his joy.

'Twas brillig, and the slithy toves
    Did gyre and gimble in the wabe:
All mimsy were the borogoves,
    And the mome raths outgrabe.

Lewis Carroll
(from *Alice Through the Looking-Glass*)

The Trees Are Growing High

The trees are growing high, my love, and the grass is
                                        growing green.
'Tis many a cold and winter's night that I alone have
                                                been.
It is a cruel and bitter night that I must lie alone
For my bonny boy is young but he's growing.

Oh father, dear father, I think you did me wrong
For to go and get me married to one who is so young,
For he is but sixteen years and I am twenty-one –
Oh, my bonny boy is young and still growing.

Oh daughter, dearest daughter, I did not do you wrong
For to go and get you married to one who is so young,
For he will be a match for you when I am dead and gone.
Yes, the bonny boy is young, but he's growing.

Oh father, dear father, I'll tell you what I'll do.
I'll send my boy to college for another year or two,
And all around his college cap I'll bind a ribbon blue
For to let the ladies know that he's growing.

A year it went by, and I passed the college wall.
I saw the young collegians a-playing at the ball.
I spied my love amongst them, the fairest of them all –
The bonny boy is young, but he's growing.

At the age of sixteen years he was a married man,
And at the age of seventeen the father of a son,
But at the age of eighteen o'er his grave the grass grew
green —
Cruel death put an end to his growing.

I'll make my love a shroud of the ornamental brown,
And every stitch I put in it the tears they will run down,
For once I had a true love and now he's lying low,
But I'll watch o'er his boy while he's growing.

Traditional

Dingo Dingo

She ran, swift and low, at the close of the day,
Testing the wind, her head held high
The far-away plain was her nightly run,
And back in the cave the young pups whined.

She moved like a wraith through the desert gums,
Skirting the creek where tracks would show,
Threading her way through rock-strewn ground,
The miles passed under her running stride.

The man lay flat at the foot of the cave,
The rifle held in his slender hands,
Stealth and patience were part of him,
Hat pulled low to shutter the moon.

She came through the gap at the edge of the plain,
Looked at the sheep with hungry eyes:
Sank on her belly, creeping up close,
Pointing her ears at the sleeping prey.

The moonlight captured the scene of death,
She sprang at the throat of the nearest lamb.
The old ewe turned, too late, too late,
And met the same fate as her dying young.

The dingo gorged on the flesh of the kill,
Picked up the lamb in her trap-like jaws
And began her run to the distant cave
With the food she'd won for her hungry ones.

A blood-red dawn had painted the east
When at last she reached the edge of the range.
She paused and tested the air about her
Then soft and clear she called to her young.

In an instant, frozen, she saw the Man
Between herself and the secret cave;
She dropped the lamb as the bullet struck
Her yellow coat ran crimson then.

The rising sun caught the scene of death.
The hunter deftly handled the kill:
He thought of what he could buy his young
And with a smile he turned for home.

Jack Davis

The Wreck of the Hesperus

It was the schooner Hesperus,
 That sailed the wintry sea;
And the skipper had taken his little daughter,
 To bear him company.

Blue were her eyes as the fairy-flax,
 Her cheeks like the dawn of day,
And her bosom white as the hawthorn buds
 That ope in the month of May.

The skipper he stood beside the helm,
 His pipe was in his mouth,
And he watched how the veering flaw did blow
 The smoke now West, now South.

Then up and spake an old Sailor,
 Had sailed the Spanish Main,
'I pray thee, put into yonder port,
 For I fear a hurricane.

'Last night the moon had a golden ring,
 And to-night no moon we see!'
The skipper he blew a whiff from his pipe,
 And a scornful laugh laughed he.

Colder and colder blew the wind,
 A gale from the North-east;
The snow fell hissing in the brine,
 And the billows frothed like yeast.

Down came the storm, and smote amain,
    The vessel in its strength;
She shuddered and paused, like a frightened steed,
    Then leaped her cable's length.

'Come hither! come hither! my little daughter,
    And do not tremble so;
For I can weather the roughest gale,
    That ever wind did blow.'

He wrapped her warm in his seaman's coat
    Against the stinging blast;
He cut a rope from a broken spar,
    And bound her to the mast.

'O father! I hear the churchbells ring,
    O say, what may it be?'
'Tis a fog-bell on a rock-bound coast!'–
    And he steered for the open sea.

'O father! I hear the sound of guns,
    O say, what may it be?'
'Some ship in distress, that cannot live
    In such an angry sea!'

'O father! I see a gleaming light,
    O say, what may it be?'
But the father answered never a word,
    A frozen corpse was he.

Lashed to the helm, all stiff and stark,
    With his face turned to the skies,
The lantern gleamed through the gleaming snow
    On his fixed and glassy eyes.

Then the maiden clasped her hands and prayed
      That savèd she might be;
And she thought of Christ, who stilled the wave,
      On the Lake of Galilee.

And fast through the midnight dark and drear,
      Through the whistling sleet and snow,
Like a sheeted ghost, the vessel swept
      Towards the reef of Norman's Woe.

And ever the fitful gusts between
      A sound came from the land;
It was the sound of the trampling surf,
      On the rocks and the hard sea-sand.

The breakers were right beneath her bows,
      She drifted a dreary wreck,
And a whooping billow swept the crew
      Like icicles from her deck.

She struck where the white and fleecy waves
      Looked soft as carded wool,
But the cruel rocks, they gored her side
      Like the horns of an angry bull.

Her rattling shrouds, all sheathed in ice,
      With the masts went by the board;
Like a vessel of glass, she stove and sank,
      Ho! Ho! the breakers roared!

At daybreak, on the bleak sea-beach,
      A fisherman stood aghast,
To see the form of a maiden fair,
      Lashed close to a drifting mast.

The salt sea was frozen on her breast,
    The salt tears in her eyes;
And he saw her hair, like the brown sea-weed,
    On the billows fall and rise.

Such was the wreck of the Hesperus,
    In the midnight and the snow!
Christ save us all from a death like this
    On the reef of Norman's Woe!

Henry Wadsworth Longfellow

The Wizard of Alderley Edge

From Mobberley on a bright morning,
On a snow-white pure-bred mare,
A farmer rode to Macclesfield
For to sell her at the fair.

Over Alderley Edge he took a path
Where the day is endless night
But the mare did halt in a shroud of mist
For a man all clad in white.

CHORUS

From Macclesfield to Mobberley,
If you have wares to sell,
Don't leave the path at The Wizard's Inn
Or drink at The Wizard's Well.

'Well met,' said the man as he stood in the path,
'Won't you sell to me your mare?'
But the farmer said, 'She's not for sale
Till I get to Macclesfield Fair.'

'Well, you can stay all day at the fair
But no bidding will you hear.
I'll wait for you in this very same place
As evening does draw near.'

Now this farmer was a puzzled man
As he rode into Macclesfield town,
For admiring glances all that day
Wouldn't fill his purse with crowns.

And he rode home a bitter man,
As the sun fell in the sky,
And just as he had said that morn,
The wizard did draw nigh.

'Now you must sell to me your mare
For silver and bright gold,'
As he led the farmer and his mare
Down a path so dark and cold.

And they passed through some iron gate
And through a great black wall,
Like moles they went lying double-bent
Till they came to The Sleepers' Hall.

In fear this farmer he did gaze
And loudly he did moan,
Four full-dressed knights each one with mount
Except for one alone.

'These are King Arthur's gallant men
Who wait on England's need,
So fill your purse and leave your mare
And leave The Edge with speed.'

Though he left The Edge a very rich man
His story caused him pain
And those who would search for the iron gate
Will search the day in vain.

But some do say that old Nell Beck
Did find the iron gate,
But most say that she stricken was
With a March-hare as her mate.

Traditional

74

Miss Peacock

'You shut that umbrella, my girl, in this gale;
It'll turn inside out…
I could tell you a tale…
That stubborn Miss Peacock would keep up her brolly
In spite of a wind that clawed you like holly,
And the gale got inside, she was swept off her feet
And towed limp and helpless along the main street,
Lifted up in the air in front of the people,
And got pecked on the knee by the cock on the steeple,
Carried over the fields, the hills… what a dance,
Until, so they say, she alighted in France.

So,
Listen to Mother, don't whine and don't wince;
That Miss Peacock, my girl, we've never seen since.'

Gregory Harrison

The Train to Glasgow

Here is the train to Glasgow.

Here is the driver,
Mr MacIver,
Who drove the train to Glasgow.

Here is the guard from Donibristle
Who waved his flag and blew his whistle
To tell the driver,
Mr MacIver,
To start the train to Glasgow.

Here is a boy called Donald MacBrain
Who came to the station to catch the train
But saw the guard from Donibristle
Wave his flag and blow his whistle
To tell the driver,
Mr MacIver,
To start the train to Glasgow.

Here is a guard, a kindly man
Who, at last moment, hauled into the van
That fortunate boy called Donald MacBrain
Who came to the station to catch the train
But saw the guard from Donibristle
Wave his flag and blow his whistle
To tell the driver,
Mr MacIver,
To start the train to Glasgow.

Here are hens and here are cocks,
Clucking and crowing inside a box,
In charge of the guard, that kindly man
Who, at the last moment, hauled into the van
That fortunate boy called Donald MacBrain
Who came to the station to catch the train
But saw the guard from Donibristle
Wave his flag and blow his whistle
To tell the driver,
Mr MacIver,
To start the train to Glasgow.

Here is the train, It gave a jolt
Which loosened a catch and loosened a bolt,
And let out the hens and let out the cocks,
Clucking and crowing out of their box,
In charge of the guard, that kindly man
Who, at the last moment, hauled into the van
That fortunate boy called Donald MacBrain
Who came to the station to catch the train
But saw the guard from Donibristle
Wave his flag and blow his whistle
To tell the driver,
Mr MacIver,
To start the train to Glasgow.

The guard chased a hen and, missing it, fell.
The hens were all squawking, the cocks as well,
And unless you were there you haven't a notion
The flurry, the fuss, the noise and commotion
Caused by the train which gave a jolt
And loosened a catch and loosened a bolt
And let out the hens and let out the cocks,
Clucking and crowing out of their box,
In charge of the guard, that kindly man
Who, at the last moment, hauled into the van
That fortunate boy called Donald MacBrain
Who came to the station to catch the train
But saw the guard from Donibristle
Wave his flag and blow his whistle
To tell the driver,
Mr MacIver,
To start the train to Glasgow.

Now Donald was quick and Donald was neat
And Donald was nimble on his feet.
He caught the hens and he caught the cocks
And he put them back in their great big box.
The guard was pleased as pleased could be
And invited Donald to come to tea
On Saturday, at Donibristle
And let him blow his lovely whistle,
And said in all his life he'd never
Seen a boy so quick and clever,
And so did the driver,
Mr MacIver,
Who drove the train to Glasgow.

Wilma Horsburgh

The Goole Captain

One day as I walked by Crocodile Mansions
I met a young woman, sea-green were her eyes,
And she was loud weeping by the banks of the Humber.
O, bitter the sound of her sobs and her sighs.

I asked this young woman why she was sore weeping,
'Pray, tell me,' I said, 'why you grieve by the tide?'
And when I had put my arm tightly around her,
In a voice like a sea bird she sadly replied,

'I was born, sir, at Wetwang, but I left the East Riding,
With the cows and the sheep as a girl I would roam,
And if I were back with my fathers and brothers
I'd ne'er leave again the sweet fields of my home.'

So I led her so gently past Crocodile Mansions,
And I took her so gently by the banks of the Humber,
She gave herself freely, her eyes and her kisses,
And I gave her a gold ring and a necklet of amber.

When we parted at stardown no more was she weeping,
But the very next morning as I sailed out with the tide,
She waved to me gaily as we hove round the headland
And I yearned for her beauty to be by my side.

O, I sailed for a year and a day to the Indies
And I came back to England one green day in spring
But I had forgotten the girl with the green eyes,
The necklet of amber, the little gold ring.

But as I was strolling down the Land of Green Ginger
While our ship loaded up with a cargo for Poole,
The people they looked at me strangely and whispered,
'O, beware of the faithless young captain from Goole.'

So I went off at once to Crocodile Mansions
To look for my dear love with sea-green eyes,
But no one would tell me or answer my questions,
O, bitter my heart then and empty my sighs.

Then I met in 'The Dragon' a drunken old sailor
Who told me he'd seen her with a necklet of amber,
A little gold ring and her eyes green and staring
Floating far out to sea by the banks of the Humber.

And I walked for the last time by Crocodile Mansions,
My heart was so full I shed never a tear,
O, I looked at the sea and I looked at the Humber
And in every green wave were the eyes of my dear.

Leonard Clark

Land of Green Ginger is the name of a street in Hull,
and Wetwang is a village in the East Riding of Yorkshire.

The Shoemakker

My mother sent us to the school
to learn to be a stocking knitter
but Aa was young and played the fool
and married wi a shoemakker
shoemakker   leather cracker
wi all his stinking dirty watter
Aa wish a thousand deaths Aad died
ere Aad wed a shoemakker

his hands are like a cuddy's houghs[1]
his face is like the highlowed[2] leather
his ears are like Aa don't know what
his hair is like a buncha heather
shoemakker   leather cracker
stinking kit and rotten leather[3]
Aa wish a thousand deaths Aad died
ere Aad wed a shoemakker

he sent me for a pint of wine
and Aa brought him a pint of watter
but he played me as good a trick
he made my shoes arotten leather
shoemakker   leatherstrapper
three rows arotten leather
balls of wax and stinking watter
who would have a shoemakker?

Anon

[1]donkey's hocks   [2]shiny   [3]resin, pitch and tallow mixture.

Mr Simpson and His Cat

Old Mr Simpson lived alone
But not precisely on his own.
The best way to make sense of that
Is to explain he kept a cat.
That is, he kept her warm and fed,
But she kept him, it should be said,
From – well, from going off his head
With loneliness and lovelessness.
She was quite plain, I must confess,
Black as the ace of spades, without
A fleck of white from tail to snout,
No pretty ways, no clever tricks,
Called Floss. But wait. Each night at six,
When Mr Simpson took his tot
Of gin, he'd offer her a shot:
'Come on, old Flossie, try a sip,
Simply for the companionship.'
But no, she wouldn't turn a hair,
She'd just pretend he wasn't there;
Most disappointing. Ah, but then
There came a gloomy evening when
The north wind had begun to blow,
The streets were dark and deep in snow,
And, almost wishing he were dead,
Old Simpson poured his gin and said,
'Well, Flossie, would you like a shot?'
And clearly heard her say, 'Why not?'
So then they settled down to chat
Of kittens, neighbours, dogs, all that,

Of all the years they'd spent together
And faced their share of stormy weather,
How Floss was once stuck in a tree,
And Mr Simpson got her free,
The time he fell and hit his head,
And Floss yowled fit to wake the dead
Until the upstairs tenant's wife
Heard her – which saved the old boy's life.
The time went by, I rather think
They must have had another drink
And Mr Simpson thereupon
Put some of his old records on,
And said to Flossie, 'Shall we dance?'
And with fantastic elegance
The pair of them moved to and fro
(With slow and slow and quick-quick slow)
Across that little sitting-room
To 'Sweetie Pie' and 'Love in Bloom'.
The hour of midnight came at last,
The time of wonderland was past;
Old Simpson sank into his chair,
And some hours later woke up there
Feeling distinctly worse for wear.
What he remembered of last night
Seemed crazy in the morning light;
A dream, he thought – he knew it was
As soon as Flossie showed, because
When he called, 'Hallo, my dear,'
She hardly found it worth a sneer;
She didn't even turn a hair,
Pretended he just wasn't there.

Well, so it goes, he thought, that's that;
Of course, she's no more than a cat.
That morning, following routine,
Mrs Malone came in to clean,
And, as she always did, picked up
Old Mr Simpson's coffee-cup,
His empty glass – but half a minute,
There was a second glass, and in it
A dozen strands of jet-black hair.
Mrs Malone said, 'I declare!
That's something to be wondered at!
No one comes here; there's just the cat.'

Kingsley Amis

Sir Patrick Spens

The King sits in Dunfermline toun,
    A drinking at the wine.
'O where shall I get a skilly skipper
    To sail this ship o mine?'

Then up and spak an eldern carle
    Stood by the King's right knee.
'Sir Patrick Spens is the best sailor
    That ever sailed the sea.'

The King has written a lang letter
    And signed it wi his hand,
And sent it to young Patrick Spens
    Was walking on Leith sands.

The first line that Sir Patrick read
    A loud laugh laughèd he.
The next line that Sir Patrick read
    The tear blinded his ee.

'Tae Norrowa, tae Norrowa,
    Tae Norrowa o'er the faem,
The King's daughter frae Norrowa,
    'Tis ye maun brang her hame.'

'O Wha is this done this ill deed,
    And telled the King o me?
Although it were my ain father
    An ill death may he dee.'

They hadna been in Norrowa
  A week but barely three
When all the Lords o Norrowa
  They up and spak sae free.

'These outland Scots waste our King's gold
  And swalla our Queen's fee.'
Wearie fa the tongue that spak
  Sicca mortal lee.

'Tak tent, tak tent, my good men all,
  Our good ship sails the morne.'
'O say na sae, my master dear,
  For I fear a deadly storm.

'Late late yestreen I saw the new moon
  Wi the auld moon in her arm.
I fear, I fear, my dear master
  That we shall come to harm.'

O laith laith were those good Scots Lords
  To wet their cork-heeled shoon,
But long e'er all the play was played
  They wet their hats aboon.

O lang lang may their ladies sit
  Wi their gold fans in their hand
Waiting for Sir Patrick Spens
  Come sailing to the land.

O lang lang may their ladies sit
    Wi the gold combs in their hair
Waiting for their own dear lords,
    They'll see them never mair.

Haf owre, haf owre, by Aberdour,
    Where the sea's sae wide and deep,
It's there it lies Sir Patrick Spens
    Wi the Scots Lords at his feet.

Anon

The Homecoming

The mountain glittered, its golden veins bright
As seven pick-axes attacked it with might.

Shrill rings of iron on rock sang loud
From seven hard strikes as seven backs bowed.

The precious lode weakened with every blow
But seven rush torches were burning low;

Long shadows danced on the cavern's dome
So seven grey beards all turned for home.

In a line they strode the forest path
Seven grimed bodies in need of a bath!

Low branches dripped the day's rain down
But seven lined foreheads creased in a frown,

For smoke curled out of the chimney stack
And seven stern faces were taken aback.

At the edge of the forest they paused and spied,
Then seven vexed voices: 'unnatural' they cried!

So tall, so slim, such unwhiskered cheeks,
Seven jaws drop as the young girl speaks:

'Oh! What dear little folk do I see?' –
All seven take fright, then scatter and flee.

She turns, forlorn, and enters the house
So the seven creep back, as quiet as a mouse.

On tiptoes they stand: through the window they look,
Seven pairs of eyes all watching her cook.

A fine feast for kings she did prepare
Causing seven keen noses to sniff the air.

She opened the door and beckoned them in,
Then seven loud voices were raised in a din.

But soon they were seated in all the right places
And seven large plates were raised to their faces.

When the meal was over they got ready for bed
And seven gruff voices in unison said…

'We've decided we like you and hope you won't go',
Then seven to bed, soon asleep in a row.

Matilda Webb

Kopakona – Seal-Woman

(a Faroese legend)

I'd heard the story that they come ashore
    On the Twelfth Night,
And that year I was standing by the door
Looking into the dark; I wanted a sight
Of new year stars that might be shining out
From the deep winter sky that hid the world
Of mountain, valley, stream and lake and sea.
When dark moved against dark I had no doubt
That they had come; my hand behind me pulled
The door closed. I knew they could not see me.

Down by the shore, a low form, then another,
    Out of the sea
They came, a group of ten or twelve, closer,
On to the grass above the rocks. I could see
Round heads, soft eyes and mournful colonel whiskers
In the window's glow. The sheen of their black skin
Polished curves in the dark. Then suddenly
From each shape a new form stepped, white fires
Flowed up to my shoulder's height, moved in
To a circle of figures dancing on two limbs, free.

As they danced they sang a wild song,
    Aeolian harps
Telling of winds and caves and lives that belong
To the water world of calms and storms and deeps.
I followed as they moved away and saw
Left on the grass black shadows, their cast-off skins.

Moved by desire I took one up and stole
Into my house with it, locked in a drawer
An identity, feeling as one who wins
A prize from another world that will make him whole.

The dance was ending, they were coming near,
    Back to the shore,
Resuming their fluid forms for the rest of the year.
One who stayed searching, still human-limbed,
    Was more
Lithe than all the rest, I had captured the queen.
Sure of her now, I waited until she fell
Grieving and pleading to the black rocks, the hard
Merciless ground that offered only the green
Brief growth of the grass, the sweet dusty hay,
And the stubborn soil that took life and death
    from the seed.

But as man my hands could offer her my life –
    In exchange for hers:
I went to her, wrapped her in wool, a wife
Drawn from the sea. I would give her furs,
Fish in abundance, milk, bread and a fire
That would never be slaked while she graced my house
With her beauty and her body's bounty. Her eyes
In one deep glance understood my desire,
Accepted her plight, followed me into the place
She was to fill with duties and children and days.

Years passed and I had forgotten the life of the sea,
    Kopakona's world –
Everyone knew her a human wife to me,
She had few friends, the children kept her time filled.

Sometimes, coming in, I would see her gazing out
Over the sea, a dream in her face that was strange
To me. But I did not think that she grieved.
I forgot to lock the drawer, having no doubt
That she was content. Did not know she would change
Her life with me for the sea-life for which she starved.

I was bitter. No better than eel or lemming, I swore
    She had gone
Blindly following instinct, nothing more,
None of the human love and laws I'd shown
Her had lodged in her animal brain. I took
A village woman to care for the children she left
And tried to ignore my heart that spoke of the theft
Of a life's identity, of imposing a thick
Thatch of imprisonment on the weft
Of another's spirit. But once, when I had wept

Alone at night she spoke to me in sleep:
    'If you loved
Me and the years I gave, care to keep
Some tenderness of memory, see they are saved,
My kin here now, from the seal-hunters' knives.'

I woke late, heavy-eyed, went to the boats,
But the hunters had gone early out to the caves
Where the seals sheltered. When I came there the cries
Of killers and killed were silent, blood from slit throats
Crimsoned the sea. The voices of waves,

The seabird's howl, the bitter lamenting wind,
    All accused me.
The hunters called me, showed me a strange find,
A golden chain hung with a twisted key
They had taken from a she-seal's neck, the last
That they had killed. 'Such eyes the creature had,
You could almost think it human. Well, home again.
Gale-warning today.' I followed slowly, lost
Was my hope of freeing one who had once
    followed me,
Even in death bound by my golden chain.

Anne Born

The Wind – tapped like a tired Man

The Wind – tapped like a tired Man –
And like a Host – 'Come in'
I boldly answered – entered then
My Residence within

A Rapid – footless Guest –
To offer whom a Chair
Were as impossible as hand
A Sofa to the Air –

No Bone had He to bind Him –
His Speech was like the Push
Of numerous Humming Birds at once
From a superior Bush –

His Countenance – a Billow –
His Fingers, as He passed
Let go a music – as of tunes
Blown tremulous in Glass –

He visited – still flitting –
Then like a timid Man
Again, He tapped – 'twas flurriedly –
And I became alone –

Emily Dickinson

Little Billee

There were three sailors of Bristol city
Who took a boat and went to sea,

But first with beef and captain's biscuits
And pickled pork they loaded she.

There was gorging Jack and guzzling Jimmy,
And the youngest he was little Billee.

Now when they got as far as the Equator
They'd nothing left but one split pea.

Says gorging Jack to guzzling Jimmy,
'I am extremely hungaree.'

To gorging Jack says guzzling Jimmy,
'We've nothing left; us must eat we.'

Says gorging Jack to guzzling Jimmy,
'With one another we shouldn't agree!

'There's little Bill, he's young and tender,
We're old and tough, so let's eat he.'

'Oh, Bill, we're going to kill and eat you,
So undo the button of your chemie.'

When Bill received this information
He used his pocket handkerchie.

'First let me say my catechism,
Which my poor mammy taught to me.'

'Make haste, make haste,' says guzzling Jimmy,
While Jack pulled out his snickersnee.

So Billy went up to the main-top gallant mast,
And down he fell on his bended knee.

He scarce had come to the twelfth commandment
When up he jumps. 'There's land I see:

'There's Jerusalem and Madagascar,
And North and South Amerikee:

'There's the British flag a-riding at anchor,
With Admiral Napier, K.C.B.'

So when they got aboard of the Admiral's,
He hanged fat Jack and flogged Jimmee:

But as for little Bill, he made him
The Captain of a Seventy-three.

William Makepeace Thackeray

The Cap and Bells

The jester walked in the garden:
The garden had fallen still;
He bade his soul rise upward
And stand on her windowsill.

It rose in a straight blue garment,
When owls began to call:
It had grown wise-tongued by thinking
Of a quiet and light footfall;

But the young queen would not listen;
She rose in her pale nightgown;
She drew in the heavy casement
And pushed the latches down.

He bade his heart go to her,
When the owls called out no more;
In a red and quivering garment
It sang to her through the door.

It had grown sweet-tongued by dreaming
Of a flutter of flower-like hair;
But she took up her fan from the table
And waved it off on the air.

'I have cap and bells,' he pondered,
'I will send them to her and die';
And when the morning whitened
He left them where she went by.

She laid them upon her bosom,
Under a cloud of her hair,
And her red lips sang them a love-song
Till stars grew out of the air.

She opened her door and her window,
And the heart and the soul came through.
To her right hand came the red one,
To her left hand came the blue.

They set up a noise like crickets,
A chattering wise and sweet,
And her hair was a folded flower
And the quiet of love in her feet.

W B Yeats

Jack and the Beanstalk

Jack's mother said, 'We're *stony broke*!
'Go out and find some wealthy bloke
'Who'll buy our cow. Just say she's sound
'And worth at least a hundred pound.
'But don't you dare to let him know
'That she's as old as billy-o.'
Jack led the old brown cow away,
And came back later in the day,
And said, 'Oh mumsie dear, guess what
'Your clever little boy has got.
'I got, I really don't know how,
'A super trade-in for our cow.'
The mother said, 'You little creep
'I'll bet you sold her much too cheap.'
When Jack produced one lousy bean,

His startled mother, turning green,
Leaped high up in the air and cried,
'I'm *absolutely stupefied!*
'You crazy boy! D' you really mean
'You sold our Daisy for a bean?'
She snatched the bean. She yelled, 'You chump!'
And flung it on the rubbish-dump.
Then summoning up all her power,
She beat the boy for half an hour,
Using (and nothing could be meaner)
The handle of a vacuum-cleaner.
At ten p.m. or thereabout,
The little bean began to sprout.
By morning it had grown so tall
You couldn't see the top at all.
Young Jack cried, 'Mum admit it now!
'It's better than a rotten cow!'
The mother said, 'You lunatic!
'Where are the beans that I can pick?
'There's not *one bean!* It's bare as bare!'
'No no!' cried Jack. 'You look up there!
'Look very high and you'll behold
'Each single leaf is solid gold!'
By gollikins, the boy was right!
Now, glistening in the morning light,
The mother actually perceives
A mass of lovely golden leaves!
She yells out loud, 'My sainted souls!
'I'll sell the Mini, buy a Rolls!
'Don't stand and gape, you little clot!
'Get up there quick and grab the lot!'
Jack was nimble, Jack was keen.

He scrambled up the mighty bean.
Up up he went without a stop,
But just as he was near the top,
A ghastly frightening thing occurred –
Not far above his head he heard
A big deep voice, a rumbling thing
That made the very heavens ring.
It shouted loud, 'FEE FI FO FUM
'I SMELL THE BLOOD OF AN ENGLISHMAN!'
Jack was frightened, Jack was quick,
And down he climbed in half a tick.
'Oh mum! he gasped. 'Believe you me
'There's something nasty up our tree!
'I saw him, mum! My gizzard froze!
'A Giant with a clever nose!'
'A *clever nose!*' his mother hissed.
'You must be going round the twist!'
'He smelled me out, I swear it mum!
'He said he *smelled* an Englishman!'
The mother said, 'And well he might!
'I've told you every single night
'To take a bath because you smell,
'But would you do it? Would you hell!
'You even make your mother shrink
'Because of your unholy stink!'
Jack answered, 'Well if you're so clean
'Why don't *you* climb the crazy bean,'
The mother cried, 'By gad, I will!
'There's life within the old dog still!'

She hitched her skirts above her knee
And disappeared right up the tree.
Now would the Giant smell his mum?
Jack listened for the *fee-fo-fum.*
He gazed aloft. He wondered when
The dreaded words would come... And then...
From somewhere high above the ground
There came a frightful crunching sound.
He heard the Giant mutter twice,
'By gosh, that tasted very nice.
'Although' (and this in grumpy tones)
'I wish there weren't so many bones.'
'By Christopher!' Jack cried. 'By gum!
'The Giant's eaten up my mum!
'He smelled her out! She's in his belly!
'I had a hunch that she was smelly.'
Jack stood there gazing longingly
Upon the huge and golden tree.
He murmured softly, 'Golly-gosh,
'I guess I'll *have* to take a wash
'If I am going to climb this tree
'Without the Giant smelling me.
'In fact, a bath's my only hope...'
He rushed indoors and grabbed the soap
He scrubbed his body everywhere.
He even washed and rinsed his hair.
He did his teeth, he blew his nose
And went out smelling like a rose.
Once more he climbed the mighty bean.

The Giant sat there, gross, obscene,
Muttering through his vicious teeth
(While Jack sat tensely just beneath),
Muttering loud, 'FEE FI FO FUM,
'RIGHT NOW I CAN'T SMELL ANYONE.'
Jack waited till the Giant slept,
Then out along the boughs he crept
And gathered so much gold, I swear
He was an instant millionaire.
'A bath,' he said, 'does seem to pay.
'I'm going to have one every day.'

Roald Dahl

La Belle Dame Sans Merci

O, what can ail thee, knight at arms,
    Alone and palely loitering;
The sedge has withered from the lake,
    And no birds sing.

O, what can ail thee, knight at arms,
    So haggard and so woe-begone?
The squirrel's granary is full,
    And the harvest's done.

I see a lily on thy brow
    With anguish moist and fever-dew,
And on thy cheeks a fading rose
    Fast withereth too.

I met a lady in the meads,
    Full beautiful – a faery's child,
Her hair was long, her foot was light,
    And her eyes were wild.

I made a garland for her head,
    And bracelets too, and fragrant zone,
She looked at me as she did love,
    And made sweet moan.

I set her on my pacing steed
    And nothing else saw all day long;
For sideways would she lean, and sing
    A faery's song.

She found me roots of relish sweet,
    And honey wild and manna dew;
And sure in language strange she said –
    I love thee true.

She took me to her elfin grot,
    And there she gazed and sighed full sore:
And there I shut her wild, wild eyes
    With kisses four.

And there she lullèd me asleep,
    And there I dreamed, ah woe betide,
The latest dream I ever dreamed
    On the cold hill side.

I saw pale kings and princes too,
    Pale warriors, death-pale were they all:
They cry'd – 'La belle Dame sans Merci
    Hath thee in thrall!'

I saw their starved lips in the gloam
    With horrid warning gapèd wide,
And I awoke, and found me here
    On the cold hill side.

And this is why I sojourn here
    Alone and palely loitering,
Though the sedge is withered from the lake,
    And no birds sing.

John Keats

Thomas the Scarecrow

In a field by a castle an old scarecrow stands
With a stick for its body and twigs for its hands
Its head is a turnip that swings with the wind
And they call it Thomas the Scarecrow.
His tall hat is battered, his long coat is torn
As he stands with his arms stretched and watches the corn
The birds fly around for he means them no harm
And they perch on Thomas the Scarecrow.

As he looks out through the holes of his eyes
A beautiful girl at a window he spies
And out in the cornfields a love starts to grow
In the heart of Thomas the Scarecrow.
She was a princess so young and so fair
With dresses of fine silk and long golden hair
And soon all the birds would gather to hear
Of the love of Thomas the Scarecrow.

He asked the swallow to find some fine flower
And carry it up to his own true love's bower
And tell her it came from one who loved dear
And the bird flew from Thomas the Scarecrow.
He took in his beak the wild rose so fair
For the Princess to put in her long golden hair
Told her it came from one who loved true
And the name of Thomas he gave her.

She smiled to think of the handsome young man
Whose token of love she held in her hand
And a ribbon she drew from her long golden hair
For the swallow to take to its master.
Each day the swallow would search all around
Till some new pretty flower in the hedgerow he'd found
With all of the wildflowers the princess was wooed
For the sake of Thomas the Scarecrow.

One day the Princess decided that she
Would see who her handsome young lover might be
And on her grey pony in hiding she stayed
Till the swallow flew out from her window.
The swallow flew over the meadows so high
And she followed in hope that her love she would spy
When sudden the swallow dropped down from the sky
And lighted on Thomas the Scarecrow.

The Princess drew near but did not understand
Till she saw her own ribbon in the twigs of her hands
And she wept to discover her love was no man
But only Thomas the Scarecrow.
That night on her pillow as pale as the cream
She wept for the handsome young man of her dreams
And outside rain lashed and the wind it did scream
And they beat on Thomas the Scarecrow.

After that night of the wind and the rain
Thomas the Scarecrow was ne'er seen again
But on the next morning a willow tree stood
In the place of Thomas the Scarecrow.
And under that tree for many a year
The Princess would sit all alone with her tears

And no handsome suitor could ever come near
The Princess of Thomas the Scarecrow.

All of this happened a long time ago
And over the castle ruin grass does now grow
And Princess and servants all long since laid low
And fled like Thomas the Scarecrow.
The old willow tree is all that stands there
And its branches do trail like a girl's flowing hair
With twigs for its fingers and leaves that do sigh
Like the Princess and Thomas the Scarecrow.

Gerry Doherty

Harry Eddom

High on the storm-torn coast of Iceland,
February, 'sixty-eight.
Ross Cleveland out of Hull lay hiding;
With anxious eyes her skipper waits.

Gale force twelve and the black ice building;
Blinding snow, and the radar gone –
On the cruel rocks of Isafjord
She'll be thrown before the dawn.

Try to run for the eastern seaboard –
Turn her head into the gale;
Harry Eddom leaves the wheelhouse –
Steps into that howling Hell.

Down to a grave in the icy waters –
Down to a grave in the cruel sea;
Over goes the good *Ross Cleveland* –
Ten seconds to eternity...

Out in a raft on the boiling water –
Bitter wind cuts like a knife.
Two men freeze and die beside him
As Harry Eddom clings to life.

Morning comes and the raft is grounded;
Three men lie as made of stone.
Consciousness at last returning
One man walks ashore alone...

Cold are the shores of the Isafjord,
Harsh and bare her rocky crest;
All day, all night walks Harry Eddom –
A dead man if he stops to rest.

In the misty light of an Iceland morning,
Over the rocks in the drifting rain,
Shepherds bring poor Harry Eddom
Back from the dead to sail again.

Bill Meek

from Morte d' Arthur

Then quickly rose Sir Bedivere, and ran,
And, leaping down the ridges lightly, plunged
Among the bulrush-beds, and clutched the sword,
And strongly wheeled and threw it. The great brand
Made lightnings in the splendour of the moon,
And flashing round and round, and whirled in an arch,
Shot like a streamer of the northern morn,
Seen where the moving isles of winter shock
By night, with noises of the northern sea.
So flashed and fell the brand Excalibur:
But ere he dipt the surface, rose an arm
Clothed in white samite, mystic, wonderful,
And caught him by the hilt, and brandished him
Three times, and drew him under in the mere.
And lightly went the other to the King.

    Then spoke King Arthur, drawing thicker breath:
'Now see I by thine eyes that this is done.
Speak out: what is it thou hast heard, or seen?'

    And answer made the bold Sir Bedivere:
'Sir King, I closed mine eyelids, lest the gems
Should blind my purpose, for I never saw,
Nor shall see, here or elsewhere, till I die,
Not though I live three lives of mortal men,
So great a miracle as yonder hilt.
Then with both hands I flung him, wheeling him;
But when I looked again, behold an arm,
Clothed in white samite, mystic, wonderful,

That caught him by the hilt, and brandished him
Three times, and drew him under in the mere.'

And answer made King Arthur, breathing hard:
'My end draws nigh; 'tis time that I were gone.
Make broad thy shoulders to receive my weight,
And bear me to the margin; yet I fear
My wound hath taken cold, and I shall die.'

So saying, from the pavement he half rose,
Slowly, with pain, reclining on his arm,
And looking wistfully with wide blue eyes
As in a picture. Him Sir Bedivere
Remorsefully regarded through his tears,
And would have spoken, but he found not words,
Then took care, and kneeling on one knee,
O'er both his shoulders drew the languid hands,
And rising bore him through the place of tombs.

But, as he walked, King Arthur panted hard,
Like one that feels a nightmare on his bed
When all the house is mute. So sighed the King,
Muttering and murmuring at his ear, 'Quick, quick!
I fear it is too late, and I shall die.'
But the other swiftly strode from ridge to ridge,
Clothed with his breath, and looking, as he walked,
Larger than human on the frozen hills.
He heard the deep behind him, and a cry
Before. His own thought drove him like a god.
Dry clashed his harness in the icy caves
And barren chasms, and all to left and right
The bare black cliff clanged round him, as he based
His feet on juts of slippery crag that rang

Sharp-smitten with the dint of armèd heels –
And on a sudden, lo! the level lake,
And the long glories of the winter moon.

Then saw they how there hove a dusky barge,
Dark as a funeral scarf from stem to stern,
Beneath them; and descending they were ware
That all the decks were dense with stately forms
Black-stoled, black-hooded, like a dream – by these
Three Queens with crowns of gold – and from them rose
A cry that shivered to the tingling stars,
And, as it were one voice, an agony
Of lamentation, like a wind, that shrills
All night in a waste land, where no one comes,
Or hath come, since the making of the world.

Alfred, Lord Tennyson

Ballad of the Drover

Across the stony ridges,
    Across the rolling plain,
Young Harry Dale, the drover,
    Comes riding home again.
And well his stock-horse bears him,
    And light of heart is he,
And stoutly his old packhorse
    Is trotting by his knee.

Up Queensland way with cattle
    He's travelled regions vast,
And many months have vanished
    Since home-folks saw him last.
He hums a song of someone
    He hopes to marry soon;
And hobble-chains and camp-ware
    Keep jingling to the tune.

Beyond the hazy dado
    Against the lower skies
And yon blue line of ranges
    The station homestead lies.
And thitherward the drover
    Jogs through the lazy noon,
While hobble-chains and camp-ware
    Are jingling to a tune.

An hour has filled the heavens
    With storm-clouds inky black;
At times the lightning trickles

Around the drover's track;
But Harry pushes onward,
    His horses' strength he tries,
In hope to reach the river
    Before the flood shall rise.

The thunder, pealing o'er him,
    Goes rumbling down the plain;
And sweet on thirsty pastures
    Beats fast the plashing rain;
Then every creek and gully
    Sends forth its tribute flood –
The river runs a banker,
    All stained with yellow mud.

Now Harry speaks to Rover,
    The best dog on the plains,
And to his hardy horses,
    And strokes their shaggy manes.
'We've breasted bigger rivers
    When floods were at their height,
Nor shall this gutter stop us
    From getting home tonight!'

The thunder growls a warning
    The blue, forked lightnings gleam;
The drover turns his horses
    To swim the fatal stream.
But, oh! the flood runs stronger
    Than e'er it ran before;
The saddle-horse is failing,
    And only half-way o'er!

When flashes next the lightning,
    The flood's grey breast is blank;
A cattle-dog and packhorse
    Are struggling up the bank.
But in the lonely homestead
    The girl shall wait in vain –
He'll never pass the stations
    In charge of stock again.

The faithful dog a moment
    Lies panting on the bank,
Then plunges through the current
    To where his master sank.
And round and round in circles
    He fights with failing strength,
Till, gripped by wilder waters,
    He fails and sinks at length.

Across the flooded lowlands
    And slopes of sodden loam
The packhorse struggles bravely
    To take dumb tidings home;
And mud-stained, wet, and weary,
    He goes by rock and tree,
With clanging chains and tinware
    All sounding eerily.

Traditional

The Man from Snowy River

There was movement at the station, for the word had
                                        passed around
That the colt from old Regret had got away,
And had joined the wild bush horses – he was worth a
                                        thousand pound,
So all the cracks had gathered to the fray.
All the tried and noted riders from the stations near
                                        and far
Had mustered at the homestead overnight,
For the bushmen love hard riding where the wild bush
                                        horses are,
And the stock-horse snuffs the battle with delight.

There was Harrison, who made his pile when Pardon
                                        won the cup,
The old man with his hair as white as snow;
But few could ride beside him when his blood was
                                        fairly up –
He would go wherever horse and man could go.
And Clancy of the Overflow came down to lend a hand,
No better horseman ever held the reins;
For never horse could throw him while the saddle-girths
                                        would stand –
He learnt to ride while droving on the plains.

And one was there, a stripling on a small and weedy
                                        beast;
He was something like a racehorse undersized,

With a touch of Timor pony – three parts thoroughbred
                                                    at least –
And such as are by mountain horsemen prized.
He was hard and tough and wiry – just the sort that
                                                    won't say die –
There was courage in his quick impatient tread;
And he bore the badge of gameness in his bright and
                                                    fiery eye,
And the proud and lofty carriage of his head.

But still so slight and weedy, one would doubt his
                                                    power to stay,
And the old man said, 'That horse will never do
For a long and tiring gallop – lad, you'd better stop away,
Those hills are far too rough for such as you.'
So he waited, sad and wistful – only Clancy stood his
                                                    friend –
'I think we ought to let him come,' he said:
'I warrant he'll be with us when he's wanted at the end,
For both his horse and he are mountain bred.'

'He hails from Snowy River, up by Kosciusko's side,
Where the hills are twice as steep and twice as rough;
Where a horse's hoofs strike firelight from the flint
                                                    stones every stride,
The man that holds his own is good enough.
And the Snowy River riders on the mountains make
                                                    their home,
Where the river runs those giant hills between;
I have seen full many horsemen since I first commenced
                                                    to roam,
But nowhere yet such horsemen have I seen.'

So he went; they found the horses by the big mimosa
                                          clump,
They raced away towards the mountain's brow,
And the old man gave his orders, 'Boys, go at them
                                          from the jump,
No use to try for fancy riding now.
And, Clancy, you must wheel them, try and wheel them
                                          to the right.
Ride boldly, lad, and never fear the spills,
For never yet was rider that could keep the mob in sight,
If once they gain the shelter of those hills.'

So Clancy rode to wheel them – he was racing on the wing
Where the best and boldest riders take their place,
And he raced his stock-horse past them, and he made
                                          the ranges ring
With the stockwhip, as he met them face to face.
Then they halted for a moment, while he swung the
                                          dreaded lash,
But they saw their well-loved mountain full in view,
And they charged beneath the stockwhip with a sharp
                                          and sudden dash,
And off into the mountain scrub they flew.

Then fast the horsemen followed, where the gorges
                                          deep and black
Resounded to the thunder of their tread,
And the stockwhips woke the echoes, and they fiercely
                                          answered back
From cliffs and crags that beetled overhead.
And upward, ever upward, the wild horses held their way,
Where mountain ash and kurrajong grew wide;

And the old man muttered fiercely, 'We may bid the
                                    mob good day,
No man can hold them down the other side.'

When they reached the mountain's summit, even Clancy
                                    took a pull –
It well might make the boldest hold their breath;
The wild hop scrub grew thickly, and the hidden ground
                                    was full
Of wombat holes, and any slip was death.

But the man from Snowy River let the pony have his head,
And he swung his stockwhip round and gave a cheer,
And he raced him down the mountain like a torrent
                                    down its bed,
While the others stood and watched in very fear.

He sent the flint-stones flying, but the pony kept his feet,
He cleared the fallen timber in his stride,
And the man from Snowy River never shifted in his seat –
It was grand to see that mountain horseman ride.
Through the stringy barks and saplings, on the rough
                                    and broken ground,
Down the hillside at a racing pace he went;
And he never drew the bridle till he landed safe and sound
At the bottom of that terrible descent.

He was right among the horses as they climbed the
                                    farther hill,
And the watchers on the mountain, standing mute,
Saw him ply the stockwhip fiercely; he was right among
                                    them still,

As he raced across the clearing in pursuit.
Then they lost him for a moment, where two mountain
                                        gullies met
In the ranges – but a final glimpse reveals
On a dim and distant hillside the wild horses racing yet,
With the man from Snowy River at their heels.

And he ran them single-handed till their sides were
                                        white with foam;
He followed like a bloodhound on their track,
Till they halted, cowed and beaten; then he turned their
                                        heads for home,
And alone and unassisted brought them back.
But his hardy mountain pony he could scarcely raise a
                                        trot,
He was blood from hip to shoulder from the spur;
But his pluck was still undaunted, and his courage fiery
                                        hot,
For never yet was mountain horse a cur.

And down by Kosciusko, where the pine-clad ridges
                                        raise
Their torn and rugged battlements on high,
Where the air is clear as crystal, and the white stars
                                        fairly blaze
At midnight in the cold and frosty sky,
And where around the Overflow the reed-beds sweep
                                        and sway
To the breezes, and the rolling plains are wide,
The Man from Snowy River is a household word today,
And the stockmen tell the story of his ride.

Banjo Paterson

Meeting at Night

I

The grey sea and the long black land;
And the yellow half-moon large and low;
And the startled little waves that leap
In fiery ringlets from their sleep,
As I gain the cove with pushing prow,
And quench its speed i' the slushy sand.

II

Then a mile of warm sea-scented beach;
Three fields to cross till a farm appears;
A tap at the pane, the quick sharp scratch
And blue spurt of a lighted match,
And a voice less loud, thro' its joys and fears,
Than the two hearts beating to each to each!

Robert Browning

The Two Old Women of Mumbling Hill

The two old trees on Mumbling Hill,
They whisper and chatter and never keep still.
What do they say as they lean together
In rain or sunshine or windy weather?

There were two old women lived near the hill,
And they used to gossip as women will
Of friends and neighbours, houses and shops,
Weather and trouble and clothes and crops.

Then one sad winter they both took ill,
The two old women of Mumbling Hill.
They went bent and feeble and wasted away
And both of them died on the selfsame day.

Now the ghosts of the women of Mumbling Hill,
They started to call out loud and shrill,
'Where are the tales we used to tell,
And where is the talking we loved so well?'

Side by side stood the ghosts until
They both took root on Mumbling Hill;
And they turned to trees, and they slowly grew,
Summer and winter the long years through.

In the winter the bare boughs creaked and cried,
In summer the green leaves whispered and sighed;
And still they talk of fine and rain,
Storm and sunshine, comfort and pain.

The two old trees of Mumbling Hill,
They whisper and chatter and never keep still.
What do they say as they lean together
In rain or sunshine or windy weather?

James Reeves

Fourpence A Day

The ores are waiting in the tubs, and snow's upon the
fell.
Canny folks are sleeping yet, but lead is right to sell.
Come, ye little washer lads, come, let's away,
We're bound down to slavery for fourpence a day.

It's early in the morning. We rise at at five o'clock.
The little slaves come to the door to knock, knock,
knock.
Come, ye little washer lads, come let's away,
It's very hard to work for fourpence a day.

My daddy was a miner, he lived down in the town.
'Twas hard work and poverty that always kept him
down.
He aimed for me to go to school, but brass he couldn't
pay,
So I had to go to the washing-rake for fourpence a day.

My mother rises out of bed with tears upon her cheeks,
Puts my wallet on my shoulders which has to serve a
week.
It oftens fills her great big heart when she unto me does
say:
'I never thought thou would have worked for fourpence
a day.'

Traditional

from The Pied Piper of Hamelin

Hamelin Town's in Brunswick,
By famous Hanover city;
The river Weser, deep and wide,
Washes its wall on the southern side;
A pleasanter spot you never spied;
But, when begins my ditty,
Almost five hundred years ago,
To see the townsfolk suffer so
From vermin, was a pity.

Rats!
They fought the dogs, and killed the cats,
And bit the babies in the cradles,
And ate the cheeses out of the vats,
And licked the soup from the cooks' own ladles,
Split open the kegs of salted sprats,
Made nests inside men's Sunday hats,
And even spoiled the women's chats,
By drowning their speaking
With shrieking and squeaking
In fifty different sharps and flats.

At last the people in a body
To the Town Hall came flocking:
''Tis clear,' cried they, 'our Mayor's a noddy;
And as for our Corporation – shocking
To think we buy gowns lined with ermine
For dolts that can't or won't determine
What's best to rid us of our vermin!

Rouse up, Sirs! Give your brains a racking
To find the remedy we're lacking,
Or, sure as fate, we'll send you packing!'
At this the Mayor and Corporation
Quaked with a mighty consternation.
An hour they sate in council,
At length the Mayor broke silence:
'For a guilder I'd my ermine gown sell;
I wish I were a mile hence!
It's easy to bid one rack one's brain –
I'm sure my poor head aches again
I've scratched it so, and all in vain.
Oh for a trap, a trap, a trap!'
Just as he said this, what should hap
At the chamber door but a gentle tap?
'Bless us,' cried the Mayor, 'what's that?'
(With the Corporation as he sat,
Looking little though wondrous fat;
Nor brighter was his eye, nor moister
Than a too-long-opened oyster,
Save when at noon his paunch grew mutinous
For a plate of turtle green and glutinous)
'Only a scraping of shoes on the mat?
Anything like the sound of a rat
Makes my heart go pit-a-pat!'

'Come in!' – the Mayor cried, looking bigger:
And in did come the strangest figure!
His queer long coat from heel to head
Was half of yellow and half of red;
And he himself was tall and thin,
With sharp blue eyes, each like a pin,

And light loose hair, yet swarthy skin,
No tuft on cheek nor beard on chin,
But lips where smiles went out and in –
There was no guessing his kith and kin!
And nobody could enough admire
The tall man and his quaint attire:

He advanced to the council-table:
And, 'Please your honours,' said he, 'I'm able
By means of a secret charm to draw
All creatures living beneath the sun,
That creep or swim or fly or run,
After me so as you never saw!
And I chiefly use my charm
On creatures that do people harm,
The mole and toad and newt and viper;
And people call me the Pied Piper.'
(And here they noticed round his neck
A scarf of red and yellow stripe,
To match with his coat of the self-same cheque;
And at the scarf's end hung a pipe;
And his fingers, they noticed, were ever straying
As if impatient to be playing
Upon this pipe, as low it dangled
Over his vesture so old-fangled.)
'Yet,' said he, 'poor piper as I am,
In Tartary I freed the Cham,
Last June, from his huge swarms of gnats;
I eased in Asia the Nizam
Of a monstrous brood of vampyre-bats:
And as for what your brain bewilders,
If I can rid your town of rats

Will you give me a thousand guilders?'
'One? fifty thousand!' – was the exclamation
Of the astonished Mayor and Corporation.

Into the street the Piper stept,
Smiling first a little smile,
As if he knew what magic slept
In his quiet pipe the while;
Then, like a musical adept,
To blow the pipe his lips he wrinkled,
And green and blue his sharp eyes twinkled
Like a candle-flame where salt is sprinkled;
And ere three shrill notes the pipe uttered,
You heard as if an army muttered;
And the muttering grew to a grumbling;
And the grumbling grew to a mighty rumbling;
And out of the houses the rats came tumbling.
Great rats, small rats, lean rats, brawny rats,
Brown rats, black rats, grey rats, tawny rats,
Grave old plodders, gay young friskers,
Fathers, mothers, uncles, cousins,
Cocking tails and prickling whiskers,
Families by tens and dozens,
Brothers, sisters, husbands, wives –
Followed the Piper for their lives.
From street to street he piped advancing,
And step for step they followed dancing,
Until they came to the river Weser
Wherein all plunged and perished!

You should have heard the Hamelin people
Ringing the bells till they rocked the steeple.
'Go', cried the Mayor, 'and get the long poles!

Poke out the nests and block up the holes!
Consult with carpenters and builders,
And leave in our town not even a trace
Of the rats!' – when suddenly, up the face
Of the Piper perked in the market-place,
With a 'First, if you please, my thousand guilders!'

A thousand guilders! The Mayor looked blue;
So did the Corporation too.
For council dinners made rare havoc
With Claret, Moselle, Vin-de-Grave, Hock;
And half the money would replenish
Their cellar's biggest butt with Rhenish.
To pay this sum to a wandering fellow
With a gipsy coat of red and yellow!
'Beside,' quoth the Mayor with a knowing wink,
'Our business was done at the river's brink;
We saw with our eyes the vermin sink,
And what's dead can't come to life, I think.
So, friend we're not the folks to shrink
From the duty of giving you something to drink,
And a matter of money to put in your poke;
But as for the guilders, what we spoke
Of them, as you very well know, was in joke.
Besides, our losses have made us thrifty.
A thousand guilders! Come take fifty!'

The Piper's face fell, and he cried,
'No trifling! I can't wait. Beside,
I've promised to visit by dinner time
Bagdad, and accept the prime
Of the Head-Cook's pottage, all he's rich in,

134

For having left, in the Caliph's kitchen,
Of a nest of scorpions no survivor –
With him I proved no bargain-driver,
With you, don't think I'll bate a stiver!
And folks who put me in a passion
May find me pipe to another fashion.'

'How?' cried the Mayor, 'd'ye think I'll brook
Being worse treated than a Cook?
Insulted by a lazy ribald
With idle pipe and vesture piebald?
You threaten us, fellow? Do your worst,
Blow your pipe there till you burst!'

Once more he stept into the street;
And to his lips again
Laid his long pipe of smooth straight cane;
And ere he blew three notes (such sweet
Soft notes as yet musician's cunning
Never gave the enraptured air)
There was a rustling, that seemed like a bustling
Of merry crowd justling at pitching and hustling,
Small feet were pattering, wooden shoes clattering,
Little hands clapping and little tongues chattering,
And, like fowls in a farm-yard when barley is scattering,
Out came the children running.
All the little boys and girls,
With rosy cheeks and flaxen curls,
And sparkling eyes and teeth like pearls,
Tripping and skipping, ran merrily after
The wonderful music with shouting and laughter.

The Mayor was dumb, and the Council stood
As if they were changed into blocks of wood,
Unable to move a step, or cry
To the children merrily skipping by –
And could only follow with the eye
That joyous crowd at the Piper's back.
But how the Mayor was on the rack,
And the wretched Council's bosoms beat,
As the Piper turned from the High Street
To where the Weser rolled its waters
Right in the way of their sons and daughters!

However he turned from South to West,
And to Koppelberg Hill his steps addressed,
And after him the children pressed;
Great was the joy in every breast.
'He never can cross that mighty top!
He's forced to let the piping drop,
And we shall see our children stop!'
When, lo, as they reached the mountain's side,
A wondrous portal opened wide,
As if a cavern was suddenly hollowed;
And the Piper advanced and the children followed,
And when all were in to the very last,
The door in the mountain-side shut fast.
Did I say, all? No! One was lame,
And could not dance the whole of the way;
And in after years, if you would blame
His sadness, he was used to say, –
'It's dull in our town since my playmates left!
I can't forget that I'm bereft
Of all the pleasant sights they see,

Which the Piper also promised me.
For he led us, he said, to a joyous land,
Joining the town and just at hand,
Where waters gushed and fruit-trees grew,
And flowers put forth a fairer hue,
And everything was strange and new;
The sparrows were brighter than peacocks here,
And their dogs outran our fallow deer,
And honey-bees had lost their stings,
And horses were born with eagles' wings:
And just as I became assured
My lame foot would be speedily cured,
The music stopped and I stood still,
And found myself outside the Hill,
Left alone against my will,
To go now limping as before,
And never hear of that country more!'
Alas, alas for Hamelin!

The Mayor sent East, West, North and South,
To offer the Piper by word of mouth,
Wherever it was men's lot to find him,
Silver and gold to his heart's content,
If he'd only return the way he went,
And bring the children behind him.
But when they saw 'twas a lost endeavour,
And Piper and dancers were gone for ever,
They made a decree that lawyers never
Should think their records dated duly
If, after the day of the month and the year,
These words did not as well appear,
'And so long after what happened here

On the Twenty-second of July,
Thirteen-hundred and seventy-six':
And the better in memory to fix
The place of the children's last retreat,
They called it, Pied Piper's Street –
Where any one playing on pipe or tabor
Was sure for the future to lose his labour
Nor suffered they hostelry or tavern
To shock with mirth a street so solemn;
But opposite the place of the cavern
They wrote the story on a column,
And on the great Church-Window painted
The same, to make the world acquainted
How their children were stolen away;
And there it stands to this very day.

Robert Browning

Patch-Shaneen

Shaneen and Maurya Prendergast
Lived west in Carnareagh,
And they'd a cur-dog, cabbage plot,   .
A goat, and a cock of hay.

He was five foot one or two,
Herself was four foot ten,
And he went travelling asking meal
Above through Caragh Glen.

She'd pick her bag of carrageen[1]
Or perries[2] through the surf,
Or loan an ass of Foxy Jim
To fetch her creel of turf.

Till on one windy Samhain[3] night,
When there's stir among the dead,
He found her perished, stiff and stark,
Beside him in the bed.

And now when Shaneen travels far
From Droum to Ballyhyre
The women lay him sacks or straw,
Beside the seed of fire.

And when the grey cocks crow and flap,
And winds are in the sky,
'Oh, Maurya, Maurya, are you dead?'
You'll hear Patch-Shaneen cry.

J M Synge

[1] edible seaweed   [2] periwinkles   [3] All Souls'

Flannan Isle

Though three men dwell on Flannan Isle
To keep the lamp alight,
As we steered under the lee we caught
No glimmer through the night.

A passing ship at dawn had brought
The news, and quickly we set sail
To find out what strange thing might ail
The keepers of the deep-sea light.

The winter day broke blue and bright
With glancing sun and glancing spray
While o'er the swell our boat made way,
As gallant as a gull in flight.

But as we neared the lonely Isle
And looked up at the naked height,
And saw the lighthouse towering white
With blinded lantern that all night
Had never shot a spark
Of comfort through the dark,
So ghostly in the cold sunlight
It seemed, that were struck the while
With wonder all too dread for words.
And, as into the tiny creek
We stole, beneath the hanging crag
We saw three queer black ugly birds –
Too big by far in my belief
For cormorant or shag –
Like seamen sitting bolt-upright
Upon a half-tide reef:
But as we neared they plunged from sight
Without a sound or spirt of white.

And still too mazed to speak,
We landed and made fast the boat
And climbed the track in single file,
Each wishing he were safe afloat
On any sea, however far,
So it be far from Flannan Isle:
And still we seemed to climb and climb
As though we'd lost all count of time
And so must climb for evermore;
Yet all too soon we reached the door –
The black sun-blistered lighthouse door
That gaped for us ajar.

As on the threshold for a spell
We paused, we seemed to breathe the smell
Of limewash and of tar,
Familiar as our daily breath,
As though 'twere some strange scent of death;
And so yet wondering side by side
We stood a moment still tongue-tied,
And each with black foreboding eyed
The door ere we should fling it wide
To leave the sunlight for the gloom:
Till, plucking courage up, at last
Hard on each other's heels we passed
Into the living-room.

Yet as we crowded through the door
We only saw a table spread
For dinner, meat and cheese and bread,
But all untouched and no one there;
As though when they sat down to eat,
Ere they could even taste,
Alarm had come and they in haste
Had risen and left the bread and meat,
For at the table-head a chair
Lay tumbled on the floor.

We listened, but we only heard
The feeble cheeping of a bird
That starved upon its perch;
And, listening still, without a word
We set about our hopeless search.
We hunted high, we hunted low,
And soon ransacked the empty house;

Then o'er the Island to and fro
We ranged, to listen and to look
In every cranny, cleft or nook
That might have hid a bird or mouse:
But though we searched from shore to shore
We found no sign in any place,
And soon again stood face to face
Before the gaping door,
And stole into the room once more
As frightened children steal.
Aye, though we hunted high and low
And hunted everywhere,
Of the three men's fate we found no trace
Of any kind in any place
But a door ajar and an untouched meal
And an overtoppled chair.
And as we listened in the gloom
Of that forsaken living-room —
A chill clutch on our breath —
We thought how ill-chance came to all
Who kept the Flannan Light,
And how the rock had been the death
Of many a likely lad —
How six had come to a sudden end
And three had gone stark mad,
And one, whom we'd all known as friend,
Had leapt from the lantern one still night
And fallen dead by the lighthouse wall —
And long we thought
On the three we sought,
And on what might yet befall.

Like curs a glance has brought to heel
We listened, flinching there,
And looked and looked on the untouched meal
And the overtoppled chair.

We seemed to stand for an endless while,
Though still no word was said,
Three men alive on Flannan Isle
Who thought on three men dead.

Wilfrid Gibson

Utah

Somewhere nowhere in Utah, a boy by the roadside,
gun in his hand, and the rare dumb hard tears flowing.
Beside him, the greyheaded man has let one arm slide
awkwardly over his shoulder, is talking and pointing
at whatever it is, dead, in the dust on the ground.
By the old parked Chevy, two women, talking
                                    and watching.
Their skirts flag forward. Bandannas twist with their hair.
Around them some sheep and a fence and the
                                    sagebrush burning
and burning with its blue flame. In the distance where
the mountains are clouds, lightning, but no rain.

Anne Stevenson

Bess My Badger

Bess my badger grew up
In a petshop in Leicester. Moony mask
Behind mesh. Dim eyes
Baffled by people. Customers cuddled her,

Tickled her belly, tamed her – her wildness
Got no exercise. Her power-tools,
Her minature grizzly-bear feet,
Feet like garden-forks, had to be satisfied

Being just feet,
Trudging to-fro, to-fro, in her tight cage,
Her nose brushed by the mesh, this way, that way,
All night, every night, keeping pace

With the badgers out in the woods. She was
Learning to be a prisoner. She was perfecting
Being a prisoner. She was a prisoner. Till a girl
Bought her, to free her, and sold her to me.

146

What's the opposite of taming? I'm unteaching
Her tameness. First, I shut her in a stable.

But she liked being tame. That night, as every night,
At a bare patch of wall the length of her cage
To-fro, to-fro, she wore at the wood with her nose,
Practising her prison shuffle, her jail walk.

All day, dozing in the gloom, she waited for me.
Every supper-time, all she wanted was
Me to be a badger, and romp with her in the straw.
She laughed – a chuckling sort of snarl, a rattle,

And grabbed my toe in my shoe, and held it, hard,
Then rolled on to her back to be tickled.
'Be wild,' I told her. 'Be a proper badger.'
She twisted on to her feet, as if she agreed

And listened. Her head lifted – like a hand
Shaped to cast a snake's head shadow on the wall –
What she'd heard was a car. She waddled away
Shawled in her trailing cape of grey feathers,

And looked back. Sniffed a corner. Listened.

I could see she was lonely.

                        A few nights later
Her claws went wild. And they tunnelled
From stable to stable, connecting four stables.

Then bored up through the wall so the long loft
Became her look-out. After that,
If shouting in the yard, or a tractor, disturbed her,
You'd see her peering through the dusty panes,

And if the loft door had been blown open
She'd poke her face out, furious, then slam it.
Soon she'd quarried out through the back of the stables
And with about three cartloads of stony rubble

From under the stables, she landscaped her porchway –
And the world was hers. Now, nightly,
Whatever she can shift, she'll shift, or topple,
For the worm, the beetle, or the woodlouse beneath it.

She tasted clematis roots, and now she's an addict.
She corkscrews holes in the wet lawn with her nose,
Nipping out the lobworms. With her mine-detector
Finds all the flower-bulbs. Early workmen meet her

Plodding, bowlegged, home through the village.

Already she hardly needs me. Will she forget me?
Sometimes I leave black-treacle sandwiches,
A treat at her entrance, just to remind her –
She's our houseproud lodger, deepening her rooms.

Or are we her lodgers? To her
Our farm-buildings are her wild jumble of caves,
Infested by big monkeys. And she puts up with us –
Big noisy monkeys, addicted to diesel and daylight.

Ted Hughes

Dunderbeck

Oh once there was a butcher,
    his name was Dunderbeck,
He made such tasty sausages
    that no one would suspect –
Whatever chanced to pass in reach
    Of Dunderbeck's machine,
Would flavour the butcher's sausages
    and never more be seen.

Oh Dunderbeck, oh Dunderbeck,
    how could you be so mean,
To ever have invented the
    sausage meat machine?
Now long-tailed rats and pussy-cats,
    scrawny, fat and lean,
They'll all be ground to sausage meat
    in Dunderbeck's machine.

One sunny day a little boy
    came walking in the store,
He bought a pound of sausages
    and made towards the door,
Then he began to whistle,
    he whistled up a tune,
The sausages, they jumped, they barked,
    they danced around the room.

Today the thing got busted
    the darn thing wouldn't go,
And Dunderbeck he crawled inside
    to see what made it so.
His wife came walking in just then,
    from shopping in the street,
She brushed against the starting rod
    and Dunderbeck was meat! Bang!

Traditional

The North Ship
(a legend)

I saw three ships go sailing by,
Over the sea, the lifting sea,
And the wind rose in the morning sky,
And was rigged for a long journey.

The first ship turned towards the west,
Over the sea, the running sea,
And by the wind was all possessed
And carried to a rich country.

The second turned towards the east,
Over the sea, the quaking sea,
And the wind hunted it like a beast
To anchor in captivity.

The third ship drove towards the north,
Over the sea, the darkening sea,
But no breath of wind came forth,
And the decks shone frostily.

The northern sky rose high and black
Over the proud unfruitful sea,
East and west the ships came back
Happily or unhappily:

But the third went wide and far
Into an unforgiving sea
Under a fire-spilling star,
And it was rigged for a long journey.

Philip Larkin

The Nose

The nose went away by itself
in the early morning
while its owner was asleep.
It walked along the road
sniffing at everything.

It thought: I have a personality of my own.
Why should I be attached to a body?
I haven't been allowed to flower.
So much of me has been wasted.

And it felt wholly free.
It almost began to dance
The world was so full of scents
it had had no time to notice,

when it was attached to a face
weeping, being blown,
catching all sorts of germs
and changing colour.

But now it was quite at ease
bowling merrily along
like a hoop or a wheel,
a factory packed with scent.

And all would have been well
but that, round about evening,
having no eyes for guides,
it staggered into the path
of a mouth, and it was gobbled
rapidly like a sausage
and chewed by great sour teeth –
and that was how it died.

Iain Crichton Smith
(after Gogol)

The Dying Cowboy

As I rode out by Tom Sherman's bar-room,
As I rode out so early one day,
'Twas there I espied a handsome young cowboy,
All dressed in white linen, all clothed for the grave.

'I see by your outfit that you are a cowboy,'
These words he did say as I boldly stepped by.
'Come sit down beside me and hear my sad story,
For I am shot in the breast and I know I must die.

'Then beat your drum slowly and play your fife lowly,
And play the dead march as you carry me along,
And take me to the graveyard and throw the sod o'er me,
For I'm a young cowboy and I know I've done wrong.

''Twas once in the saddle I used to go dashing,
'Twas once in the saddle I used to go gay,
But I first took to drinking and then to card-playing,
Got shot in the body and I'm dying today.

'Let sixteen gamblers come handle my coffin,
Let sixteen young cowboys come sing me a song,
Take me to the green valley and lay the sod o'er me,
For I'm a poor cowboy and I know I've done wrong.

'Go bring me back a cup of cool water
To cool my parched lips,' this cowboy then said.
Before I returned, his soul had departed
And gone to his Maker – the cowboy lay dead.

We swung our ropes slowly and rattled our spurs lowly,
And gave a wild whoop as we carried him on,
For we all loved our comrade, so brave, young and
                                    handsome,
We all loved our comrade, although he'd done wrong.

Traditional

Beauty and the Beast

A merchant, returning, remembered the gift for his
daughter,
Picked a rose from the hedge that circled my lands,
A red rose, a token.

And so fell in my power, the evil that held me,
And as gage for his life, sent me his best-loved treasure,
His white rose, his Beauty,

To be my unwilling guest. But so great was her longing
That I let her return for a month and a day,
My white rose, my beauty.

But once she was there, she forgot her promise,
Forgot her duty to me, her ugly lord,
My white rose, my captive.

The cold power of the spell and the betrayal,
The force of the broken vow broke me with grief
For my white rose, my love,

Till she, seeking her face in the glass, saw my deathbed,
Knew what she had done, flew to my side without
thinking
And I rose from my bed a prince, a man transformed
By my red rose, my love.

L J Anderson

from Christabel

'Tis the middle of the night by the castle clock,
And the owls have awakened the crowing cock;
Tu-whit! – Tu-whoo!
And hark, again! the crowing cock,
How drowsily it crew.
Sir Leoline, the Baron rich,
Hath a toothless mastiff bitch;
From a kennel beneath the rock
She maketh answer to the clock,
Four for the quarters, and twelve for the hour;
Ever and aye, by shine and shower,
Sixteen short howls, not over loud;
Some say, she sees my lady's shroud.

Is the night chilly and dark?
The night is chilly, but not dark.
The thin gray cloud is spread on high,
It covers but not hides the sky.
The moon is behind, and at the full;
And yet she looks both small and dull.
The night is chill, the cloud is gray:
'Tis a month before the month of May,
And the Spring comes slowly up this way.

The lovely lady, Christabel,
Whom her father loves so well,
What makes her in the wood so late,
A furlong from the castle gate?

She had dreams all yesternight
Of her own betrothéd knight;
And she in the midnight wood will pray
For the weal of her lover that's far away.

She stole along, she nothing spoke,
The sighs she heaved were soft and low,
And naught was green upon the oak
But moss and rarest misletoe:
She kneels beneath the huge oak tree,
And in silence prayeth she.

The lady sprang up suddenly.
The lovely lady, Christabel!
It moaned as near, as near can be,
But what it is she cannot tell. –
On the other side it seems to be,
Of the huge, broad-breasted, old oak tree.

Samuel Taylor Coleridge

On the Antrim Coast

By the time the helicopter came the whale had died,
the limb of a giant cast up on the churned sand.

All afternoon the kids had run to it with their
buckets full of sea and we had tried to turn it,

pushing our weight at its impossible mass,
willing it to find its own way back.

We felt it die against our hands like something breaking
far away. The kids stoppped in their tracks.

The helicopter turned in the grey air.

*

Sometimes a colour seeps into the water from the sky
or from the land. No one swam next day.

The sea was black. The skin of the whale had parched
and faded in the shifting tide. Other children traced its

map

of barnacles and calluses and silk while men with cameras
knelt in the sand to frame the thirty foot of it in a single

shot.

We watched from the street as our kids carried their shoes
along the strandline filling them with stones

to circle the whale, marking out its edge.

*

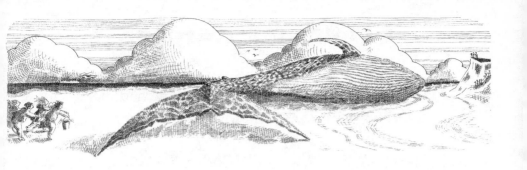

The boys drove on to the beach in a hail of sand
and long before they saw the knives the children knew.

They all backed into the sea with their hands full of
                                                    stones.
The boys ran at the whale.

Dark muscles of wave hit the shore as they stabbed
and stabbed until they severed the tail.

The children stared with ancient faces. A seagull yelled.
Then something deeper started echoing

for miles across the sand.

Amanda Dalton

Thomas Rymer

True Thomas lay on Huntlie bank,
    A ferlie he spied wi' his ee,
And there he saw a lady bright,
    Come riding down by the Eildon Tree.

Her shirt was o the grass-green silk,
    Her mantle o the velvet fyne,
At ilka tett of her horse's mane
    Hang fifty siller bells and nine.

True Thomas, he pulld aff his cap,
    And louted low down to his knee:
'All hail, thou mighty Queen of Heaven!
    For thy peer on earth I never did see.'

'O no, O no, Thomas,' she said,
    'That name does not belang to me;
I am but the queen of fair Elfland,
    That am hither come to visit thee.

'Harp and carp, Thomas,' she said,
    'Harp and carp along wi me,
And if ye dare to kiss my lips,
    Sure of your bodie I will be.'

'Betide me weal, betide me woe,
    That weird shall never daunton me;'
Syne he has kissed her rosy lips,
    All underneath the Eildon Tree.

'Now, ye maun go wi me,' she said,
    'True Thomas, ye maun go wi me,

And ye maun serve me seven years,
    Thro weal or woe, as may chance to be.'

She mounted on her milk-white steed,
    She's taen True Thomas up behind,
And aye wheneer her bridle rung,
    The steed flew swifter than the wind.

O they rade on, and farther on –
    The steed gaed swifter than the wind –
Untill they reached a desart wide,
    And living land was left behind.

'Light down, light down, now, True Thomas,
    And lean your head upon my knee;
Abide and rest a little space,
    And I will show you ferlies three.

'O see ye not yon narrow road,
    So thick beset with thorns and briers?
That is the path of righteousness,
    Tho after it but few enquires.

'And see not ye that braid braid road,
    That lies across that lily leven?
That is the path of wickedness,
    Tho some call it the road to heaven.

'And see not ye that bonny road,
    That winds about the fernie brae?
That is the road to fair Elfland,
    Where thou and I this night maun gae.

'But, Thomas, ye maun hold your tongue,
    Whatever ye may hear or see,

For, if you speak word in Elflyn land,
    Ye'll neer get back to your ain countrie.'

O they rade on, and farther on,
    And they waded thro rivers aboon the knee,
And they saw neither sun nor moon,
    But they heard the roaring of the sea.

It was mirk mirk night, and there was nae stern light,
    And they waded thro red blude to the knee;
For a' the blude that's shed on earth
    Rins thro the springs o that countrie.

Syne they came on to a garden green,
    And she pu'd an apple frae a tree:
'Take this for thy wages, True Thomas,
    It will give the tongue that can never lie.'

'My tongue is mine ain.' True Thomas said;
    'A gudely gift ye wad gie to me!
I neither dought to buy nor sell,
    At fair or tryst where I may be.

'I dought neither speak to prince or peer,
    Nor ask of grace from fair ladye:'
'Now hold thy peace,' the lady said,
    'For as I say, so must it be.'

He has gotten a coat of the even cloth,
    And a pair of shoes of velvet green,
And till seven years were gane and past
    True Thomas on earth was never seen.

Anon

The Dong with a Luminous Nose

When awful darkness and silence reign
Over the great Gromboolian plain,
 Through the long, long wintry nights; –
When the angry breakers roar
As they beat on the rocky shore; –
 When Storm-clouds brood on the towering heights
Of the Hills of the Chankly Bore: –
Then, through the vast and gloomy dark,
There moves what seems a fiery spark,
 A lonely spark with silvery rays
 Piercing the coal-black night, –
 A Meteor strange and bright: –
Hither and thither the vision strays,
 A single lurid light.

Slowly it wanders, – pauses, – creeps, –
Anon it sparkles, – flashes and leaps;
And ever as onward it gleaming goes
A light on the Bong-tree stems it throws.
And those who watch at that midnight hour
From Hall or Terrace, or lofty Tower,
Cry, as the wild light passes along, –
  'The Dong! – the Dong!
 The wandering Dong through the forest goes!
  The Dong! the Dong!
The Dong with a luminous Nose!'

Long years ago
      The Dong was happy and gay,
Till he fell in love with a Jumbly Girl
      Who came to those shores one day,
For the Jumblies came in a sieve, they did, –
Landing at eve near the Zemmery Fidd
         Where the Oblong Oysters grow,
      And the rocks are smooth and grey.
And all the woods and the valleys rang
With the Chorus they daily and nightly sang, –
      'Far and few, far and few,
      Are the lands where the Jumblies live;
      Their heads are green, and their hands are blue
      And they went to sea in a sieve.'

Happily, happily passed those days!
         While the cheerful Jumblies staid;
      They danced in circlets all night long,
      To the plaintive pipe of the lively Dong,
         In the moonlight, shine or shade.
For day and night he was always there
By the side of the Jumbly girl so fair,
With her sky-blue hands, and her sea-green hair.
Till the morning came of that hateful day
When the Jumblies sailed in their sieve away,
And the Dong was left on the cruel shore
Gazing – gazing for evermore, –
Ever keeping his weary eyes on
That pea-green sail on the far horizon, –
Singing the Jumbly Chorus still
As he sate all day on the grassy hill, –

'Far and few, far and few,
Are the lands where the Jumblies live;
Their heads are green, and their hands are blue,
And they went to sea in a sieve.'

But when the sun was low in the West,
    The Dong arose and said;–
– 'What little sense I once possessed
    Has quite gone out of my head!' –
And since that day he wanders still
By lake or forest, marsh and hill,
Singing – 'O somewhere in valley or plain
Might I find my Jumbly Girl again!
Forever I'll seek by land and shore
Till I find my Jumbly Girl once more!'
    Playing a pipe with silvery squeaks,
    Since then his Jumbly Girl he seeks,
    And because by night he could not see,
    He gathered the bark of the Twangum Tree
        On the flowery plain that grows.
        And he wove him a wondrous Nose, –
    A Nose as strange as a Nose could be!
Of vast proportions and painted red,
And tied with cords to the back of his head.
    – In a hollow rounded space it ended
    With a luminous Lamp within suspended,
        All fenced about
        With a bandaged stout
        To prevent the wind from blowing it out; –
    And with holes all round to send the light,
    In gleaming rays on the dismal night.

And now each night, and all night long,
Over those plains still roams the Dong;
And above the wail of the Chimp and Snipe
You may hear the squeak of his plaintive pipe
While ever he seeks, but seeks in vain
To meet with his Jumbly Girl again;
Lonely and wild – all night he goes, –
The Dong with a luminous Nose!
And all who watch at the midnight hour,
From Hall or Terrace, or lofty Tower,

Cry, as they trace the Meteor bright,
Moving along through the dreary night, –
    'This is the hour when forth he goes;
    The Dong with a luminous Nose!
    Yonder – over the plain he goes;
        He goes!
        He goes;
    The Dong with a luminous Nose!'

Edward Lear

By St Thomas Water

By St Thomas Water
Where the river is thin
We look for a jam-jar
To catch the quick fish in.
Through St Thomas Church-yard
Jessie and I ran
The day we took the jam-pot
Off the dead man.

On the scuffed tombstone
The grey flowers fell,
Cracked was the water,
Silent the shell.
The snake for an emblem
Swirled on the slab,
Across the beach of sky the sun
Crawled like a crab.

'If we walk,' said Jessie,
'Seven times round,
We shall hear a dead man
Speaking underground.'
Round the stone we danced, we sang,
Watched the sun drop,
Laid our hearts and listened
At the tomb-top.

Soft as thunder
At the storm's start
I heard a voice as clear as blood,
Strong as the heart.
But what words were spoken
I can never say,
I shut my fingers round my head,
Drove them away.

'What are those letters, Jessie,
Cut so sharp and trim
All round this holy stone
With earth up to the brim?'
Jessie traced the letters
Black as coffin-lead.
'He is not dead but sleeping,'
Slowly she said.

I looked at Jessie,
Jessie looked at me,
And our eyes in wonder
Grew wide as the sea.
Past the green and bending stones
We fled hand in hand,
Silent through the tongues of grass
To the river strand.

By the creaking cypress
We moved as soft as smoke
For fear all the people
Underneath awoke.
Over all the sleepers
We darted light as snow
In case they opened up their eyes,
Called us from below.

Many a day has faltered
Into many a year
Since the dead awoke and spoke
And we would not hear.
Waiting in the cold grass
Under a crinkled bough,
Quiet stone, cautious stone,
What do you tell me now?

Charles Causley

The Mouse Song

I've got a friend who's a little mouse
And he lives at the top of a little house
Little mouse
Little house
He lives at the top of a little house.

To the doctor this little mouse did go
'Cos he'd got a blister on his big right toe
Mouse did go
Big right toe
He'd got a blister on his big right toe.

'Put your toe in turpentine
And leave it there till half past nine.'
Turpentine
Half past nine
Leave it there till half past nine.

Mouse put in his foot but quite forgot –
Now three feet are all he's got.
Quite forgot
All he's got
Now three feet are all he's got.

My little mouse goes down to the shop
Hippety, hippety, hop-hop-hop.
Down to the shop
Hop-hop-hop
Hippety-hippety, hop-hop-hop.

He hopped into some wet cement
But his feet stayed put when away he went
Wet cement
Away he went
His feet stayed put when away he went.

Mouse got his nose caught in the door
And he pulled till he'd got no nose no more.
Caught in the door
Nose no more
He pulled till he'd got no nose no more.

Mouse had a bath and lost his tail
It got chewed off by a big black whale.
Lost his tail
Big black whale
It got chewed off by a big black whale.

He thought another bit just wouldn't be missed
So he sold his body to a scientist
Wouldn't be missed
Scientist
He sold his body to a scientist.

Now all day long mouse stays in bed
No feet, no body, but just his head
Stays in bed
Just his head
No feet no body but just his head.

The moral of this story my little mouse said:
'Always quit when you're a head.'
Little mouse said
You're a head
Always quit when you're a head.

Gerry Doherty

Acknowledgements

The editor and publishers gratefully acknowledge permission to reproduce the following copyright material:

The trustees of Amherst College for 'The Wind-tapped like a tired Man' by Emily Dickinson from *The Poems of Emily Dickinson*, Thomas H. Johnson, ed; (Cambridge, Mass: The Belknap Press of Harvard University Press, Copyright © 1951, 1955, 1979, 1983 by the President and Fellows of Harvard College);
Anne Born for 'Kapakona – Seal-Woman' from *Over the Bridge* (Puffin);
Carcanet Press Limited for 'Overhead in County Sligo' by Gillian Clarke from *Gillian Clarke Selected Poems*, 1985;
Amanda Dalton for 'On the Antrim Coast' from *The Dad-Baby* (Waldean Press)
Gerry Doherty for 'The Mouse Song' and 'Thomas the Scarecrow'
Victor Gollancz for 'The Nose' by Iain Crichton Smith;
HarperCollins Australia for 'Legend' by Judith Wright from her *Collected Poems*;
David Higham Associates for 'By St Thomas Water' by Charles Causley from his *Collected Poems* (Macmillan);
David Higham Associates for 'Jack and the Beanstalk' by Roald Dahl from *Revolting Rhymes* (Cape);
Gregory Harrison for 'Miss Peacock' from *Catch the Light* ed. Michael Harrison (Oxford University Press) 1982;
Humberside Leisure Services for 'Harry Eddom' by Bill Meek from *The Singing River*;
Oxford University Press for 'Utah' by Anne Stevenson from *The Collected Poems of Anne Stevenson 1955-1995*, 1996;
Laurence Pollinger for 'Mountain Lion' from *The Complete Poems of D H Lawrence*;
Penguin Books for 'Mart' from *You Tell Me*. Roger McGough and Michael Rosen (Kestrel) 1979;
Reed Books for 'The Train to Glasgow' by Wilma Horsburgh from *Clinkerdump* (Methuen Children's Books);
The Literary Trustees of Walter de la Mare, and the Society of Authors as their representative for 'The Listeners' by Walter de la Mare;
Gerda Mayer for 'Count Carrots' from *The Candy Floss Tree* (Oxford University Press)
John Murray for 'The Highwayman' by Alfred Noyes from his *Collected Poems*;
The James Reeves Estate for 'The Two Old Women of Mumbling Hill' by James Reeves from *Complete Poems for Children* (Heinemann);
A P Watt Ltd on behalf of Michael Yeats for 'The Cap and Bells' by W B Yeats from *The Collected Poems of WB Yeats*;
Matilda Webb for 'The Homecoming'

While every effort has been made to obtain permission, there may still be cases in which we have failed to trace a copyright holder. The publisher will be happy to correct any omission in future reprintings.